CHEMISTRY WORKSHOP-3

UNDERSTANDING THE CHEMISTRY OF METALS

SEYMOUR ROSEN

▶ LEARNING TRENDS · A DIVISION OF GLOBE BOOK COMPANY, INC.

THE AUTHOR

SEYMOUR ROSEN received his B. A. and M. S. degrees from Brooklyn College. He teaches science at the Edward B. Shallow Junior High School in Brooklyn.

Mr. Rosen participated in a teacher-training program for the development of science curriculum for the New York City Board of Education.

Editor: Barbara A. Branca
Project Coordination: Dimensions & Directions, Ltd.

PHOTO AND ILLUSTRATION CREDITS:
Aim Opener Art: Marion Krupp
All other drawings: Vantage Art
American Iron and Steel Institute: 122
Dept. of Energy: 86
Helena Frost: 62, 111, 115 (top), 141 (top), 143 (bottom)
Anthony Howarth, Woodfin Camp & Assoc.: Cover
N.Y. Convention and Visitors Bureau: 141 (bottom)
The Port of N.Y. Authority: 143 (top)
Reynolds Metals Co.: 41 (top), 118
U.P.I.: 41 (bottom left), 115
U.S. Steel: 41 (bottom right)

ISBN 0-87065-960-X

Copyright © 1979, Globe Book Company, Inc.
50 West 23rd Street, New York, New York 10010

Published simultaneously in Canada by
Globe/Modern Curriculum Press

Printed in the United States of America   2 3 4 5 6 7 8 9

CONTENTS

1   What is matter made of?   1

2   How are the elements listed in special order?   7

3   What parts make up an atom?   13

4   How are electrons arranged around the nucleus?   21

5   How do some compounds form?   29

6   What are the properties of metals?   37

7   What is valence?   43

8   How can valence help us to write formulas?   49

9   What is a radical?   55

10   What is a polyvalent element?   59

11   What is formula weight?   63

12   What is a chemical equation?   71

13 Does a chemical reaction destroy matter? 79

14 What is a synthesis reaction? 87

15 What is a decomposition reaction? 93

16 What is a replacement reaction? 99

17 What are oxidation and reduction? 105

18 What is an ore? 113

19 How can we free a metal from its ore? 119

20 What is an alloy? 127

21 What is metal activity? 133

22 What is corrosion? 139

23 How do we electroplate metals? 147

24 What is hard water? 155

25 How are metals important to life and health? 163

Periodic table of elements 168

List of atomic weights 170

BEFORE YOU BEGIN . . .

A silvery jet thunders overhead. An old neglected car quietly rusts in a junkyard. A blacksmith pounds a piece of iron into a horseshoe shape. A jeweler delicately places a stone into a shiny gold setting.

What do these events have in common? All of them have to do with *metals*. But metals are even more a part of your life. There is metal in your own blood right this second! Even the food you eat has metals in it.

Chemistry Workshop 3 is about the chemistry of metals and even more. It explains the tiny atoms and molecules that make up the things around us. This book tells about how different materials *react* with one another to form new materials.

This book is divided into 25 Aims. Each Aim starts with the information you'll need to know. This is followed by a series of exercises. Take your time on these. Look back to the beginning of the Aim whenever you're not sure of an answer. You'll find experiments and word games to do in the Aims, too.

WHAT IS MATTER MADE OF?

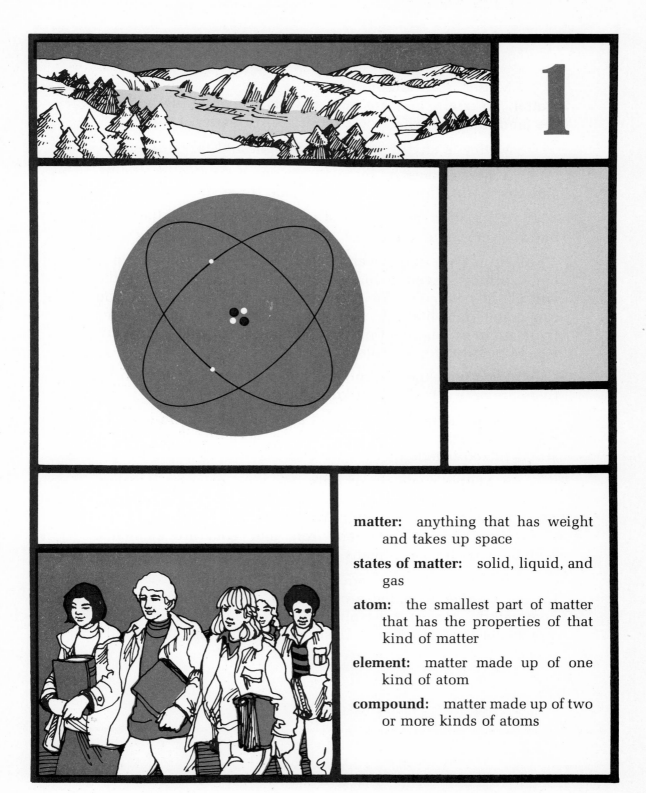

1

matter: anything that has weight and takes up space

states of matter: solid, liquid, and gas

atom: the smallest part of matter that has the properties of that kind of matter

element: matter made up of one kind of atom

compound: matter made up of two or more kinds of atoms

Matter is all around you. This book is matter. Water is matter. So is air. *You* are matter. In fact, everything you can see (and much of what you *cannot* see) is matter.

Matter is anything that has weight and takes up space.

Matter comes in three forms, or *states:* solid, liquid, and gas. *Solid, liquid,* and *gas* are the three *states of matter.*

All matter is made up of *atoms.* Atoms are called "the building blocks of matter."

Atoms are unbelievably small. A tiny bit of matter may have billions—even trillions—of atoms. The period at the end of this sentence, for example, has more atoms than you can count in a lifetime. Can you imagine how many atoms there are in *all* matter? Don't try. The number is too enormous. It is impossible to describe.

Even with the enormous *number* of atoms in the world, there are only 106 different *kinds* of atoms known.

Some matter is made up of only one kind of atom. Most matter, however, is made up of two or more different kinds of atoms *linked together.*

■ Matter made up of only one kind of atom is called an *element.* There are 106 kinds of elements. That's one element for each kind of atom. You know the names of many elements. Oxygen, hydrogen, iron, and gold are elements. Sound familiar? How many other elements can you name?

■ Matter that is made up of different kinds of atoms linked together is called a *compound.* There are millions of compounds. Almost everything you see is a compound. Water, wood, plastics—even your flesh and blood—are compounds.

NAME _____

UNDERSTANDING ATOMS AND MOLECULES

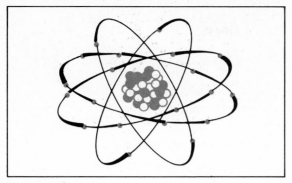

Figure A

Look at the figures. Then answer the questions.

Figure A shows a model of what scientists think an atom looks like.

The atoms of any one element are exactly *alike*. But they are *different* from the atoms of all other elements.

Different elements have different atoms.

1. What is all matter made of? _____

2. Does matter have weight and take up space? _____

3. Do atoms have weight and take up space? _____

4. How many different *kinds* of atoms are there? _____

5. What do we call matter made up of only one kind of atom? _____

6. How many elements are there? _____

7. Name three elements _____ _____ _____

8. The smallest part of an element is _____ atom of that element.
   just one, more than one

Figure B

Most matter is made up of two or more different kinds of atoms linked together.

9. What do we call matter made of different kinds of atoms linked together? _____

10. There are _____ ele-
    more, fewer
    ments than there are compounds.

11. Name three compounds.

    _____ _____

    _____

12. Does a compound have weight and take up space? _____

3

The smallest part of a compound is called a *molecule.*

Figure C shows a model of *one molecule* of water.

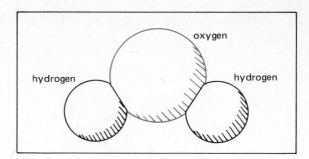

Figure C

13. How many different kinds of atoms make up a molecule of water? _____

14. Name the kinds of atoms that make up a water molecule. _____

_____

15. How many atoms of hydrogen does one molecule of water have? _____

16. How many atoms of oxygen does one molecule of water have? _____

17. Altogether, how many atoms does one molecule of water have? _____

18. The smallest part of a compound is _____ molecule of that
compound.

just one, more than one

USING SYMBOLS

The shorthand way of writing an element is called its *symbol.* The elements and their symbols are listed on page 170. Write the symbols for the following elements:

1. oxygen _____   4. hydrogen _____   7. helium _____

2. carbon _____   5. gold _____   8. silver _____

3. mercury _____   6. sodium _____   9. tin _____

The shorthand way of writing a compound is called its *formula.*

Five formulas are listed in the chart below. What are their chemical names? Choose from the following:
    magnesium oxide   copper sulfate   carbon dioxide
    silver iodide   sodium chloride

NAME _____

4

Write each name next to the correct formula. (Hint: First use page 170 to find out what each symbol stands for.)

	Formula	Chemical Name
10.	CO_2	
11.	$NaCl$	
12.	MgO	
13.	AgI	
14.	$CuSO_4$	

Figure D shows one molecule of a compound you know.

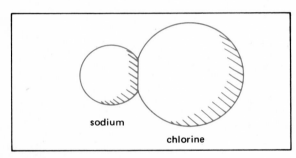

Figure D
The formula for this compound is NaCl.

15. How many atoms make up one molecule of NaCl? _____

16. Name the elements that make up NaCl. _____

_____

17. Take a guess. What is the common name of this compound? (Hint: You put it on food.) _____

Figure E shows one molecule of a compound called *sodium bicarbonate*. You know it as baking soda.

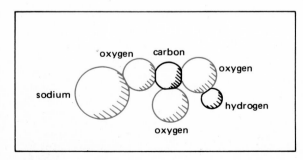

Figure E
The formula for baking soda is NaHCO_3.

18. Name the four kinds of atoms in baking soda. _____

_____   _____

_____

19. How many atoms make up one molecule of this compound? _____

A SWEET STORY

1. The formula for table sugar is $C_{12}H_{22}O_{11}$. Sugar is _____ .
   an element, a compound

2. How many different *kinds* of atoms does sugar have? _____

3. Name the elements that make up sugar. _____

   _____ _____

4. NUMBER PLEASE!
   One molecule of sugar has **a)** _____ atoms of carbon,

   b) _____ atoms of hydrogen, and

   c) _____ atoms of oxygen.

5. Altogether, how many atoms does one *molecule* of table sugar have? _____

COMPLETING SENTENCES

Complete the sentences with the choices below. One of these may be used twice.

liquid	an element	gas
compounds	molecule	atom
106	atoms	solid
space	weight	millions

1. Matter has _____ and takes up _____ .

2. The three states of matter are _____ , _____ , and

   _____ .

3. All matter is made up of _____ .

4. Matter that has only one kind of atom is called _____ .

5. There are _____ different elements. There is one element for each

   kind of _____ .

6. Linked-up atoms form matter called _____ .

7. There are _____ of compounds.

8. The smallest part of an element is just one _____ of that element.

9. The smallest part of a compound is just one _____ of that compound.

NAME _____

6

HOW ARE THE ELEMENTS LISTED IN SPECIAL ORDER?

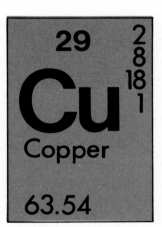

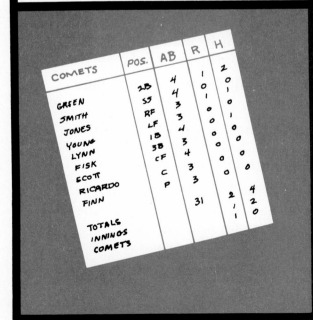

Periodic Table: a chart of the elements

property: anything about matter that helps identify it

AIM 2 | How are the elements listed in special order?

A chart lists information in an organized way. It shows many facts in a small space. Sports information is often listed on a chart—like the baseball box score. Many newspapers list the day's temperatures on a chart.

The 106 elements are listed on a special chart called the *Periodic Table*.

The Periodic Table lists the elements in order of their weights. The lighter elements are listed first. The heavier elements follow.

Each element has an *atomic number*. The atomic number tells us where an element ranks in weight. The lightest element has the lowest atomic number. The heaviest element has the highest number. The higher the atomic number, the heavier the element.

The Periodic Table has rows that run across, and columns that run down.

- Each row across is called a *period*. All the elements listed in each row belong to the same period. There are seven periods.

- Each column down is a *group* or *family*. Elements in each column belong to the same group.

Elements in the same group have many *properties* that are the same. Properties help us to identify elements. State, color, smell, and weight are examples of properties.

Each group has one column except for Group VIII. This group has three columns.

An element is either a *metal* or a *nonmetal*. On the Periodic Table, the metals are on the *left*. Nonmetals are on the *right*. There are more metals than nonmetals.

When you look at the chart, notice that hydrogen (H) is listed twice. It is listed as a metal and as a nonmetal. This is because hydrogen can act either as a metal or a nonmetal.

NAME _____

UNDERSTANDING THE PERIODIC TABLE

Check with the Periodic Table for the answers to each exercise. You can find the names of the elements on the complete chart on pages 168–169.

1. **a)** List the atomic numbers of the elements in Period 2. _____

_____

b) Write the names and symbols of these elements. _____

_____

_____

c) Which of these elements are *metals*? _____

d) Which of these elements are *nonmetals*? _____

_____

2. **a)** Name the *lightest* element in Period 2. _____

b) Name the *heaviest* element in Period 2. _____

3. To which *group* does each of these elements belong?

a) lithium _____

b) beryllium _____

c) boron _____

d) carbon _____

e) nitrogen _____

f) oxygen _____

g) fluorine _____

h) neon _____

4. a) List the *atomic numbers* of the elements in Period 3. _____

_____

b) Write the *names* and *symbols* of these elements. _____

_____

c) Which of these elements are *metals*? _____

5. a) Name the *lightest* element in Period 3. _____

b) Name the *heaviest* element in Period 3. _____

6. To which *group* does each of these elements belong?

a) sulfur _____ **e)** silicon _____

b) sodium _____ **f)** magnesium _____

c) aluminum _____ **g)** chlorine _____

d) argon _____ **h)** phosphorus _____

7. a) Name the elements in Group II B. _____

b) Which element in this group is the *heaviest*? _____

c) Which element in this group is the *lightest*? _____

8. The symbol for iron is Fe. Find iron on the Periodic Table.

a) What is the atomic number of iron? _____

b) To which *period* does iron belong? _____

c) To which *group* does iron belong? _____

d) *Name* the elements that have many properties like iron. _____

9. The symbol for calcium is Ca.

a) To which *period* does calcium belong? _____

b) To which *group* does calcium belong? _____

10. a) List the *names and symbols* of the elements that have properties similar to

calcium. _____

b) Which of these elements is the lightest? _____

c) Which of these elements is the heaviest? _____

NAME _____

FILL IN THE CHART

Fill in the chart below. The first row has been done for you.

	Element	Symbol	Atomic Number	Period	Group
1.	*Sodium*	*Na*	*11*	*3*	*IA*
2.		*O*			
3.	*Krypton*				
4.			*79*		
5.				*5*	*VIIA*
6.				*4*	*IB*

COMPLETING SENTENCES

Complete the sentences with the choices below.

heavier   group   period
nonmetal   Periodic Table   atomic
more   left   right
weight   metal   properties
family   lighter

1. The chart that lists the elements in an organized way is called the

   _____ .

2. The Periodic Table lists the elements according to _____ .

3. The number that tells us where an element ranks in weight is called the

   _____ number.

4. The lower the atomic number, the _____ the element; the higher the

   atomic number, the _____ the element.

5. Elements in the same row across belong to the same _____ .

6. Elements in the same column down belong to the same _____ or

   _____ .

7. Elements in the same group or family share important _____ .

8. An element is identified as either a _____ or a _____ .

9. On the Periodic Table, metals are on the _____. Nonmetals are on

the _____.

10. There are _____ metals than nonmetals.

MATCHING   Match the two lists. Write the correct letter on the line next to each number.

1. _____ metals and nonmetals

2. _____ Periodic Table

3. _____ atomic number

4. _____ group of elements

5. _____ period of elements

a) tells where an element ranks by weight

b) in the same row down

c) the chart of the elements

d) in the same row across

e) the two kinds of elements

Figure A   *The language of chemistry is the same all over the world.*

REACHING OUT

1. Who made up the first Periodic Table? _____

2. Where did he live? _____

3. In what year did he do it? _____

NAME _____

12

WHAT PARTS MAKE UP AN ATOM?

3

nucleus: the center part of an atom

proton: a part of the atom found inside the nucleus; a proton has a plus electrical charge.

neutron: a part of the atom found inside the nucleus; a neutron has no electrical charge.

electron: a part of the atom that moves around the nucleus; an electron has a minus electrical charge.

P = E = N

AIM 3 | What parts make up an atom?

It is hard to believe how tiny an atom is. Yet, the tiny atom is made up of even *smaller* parts. Can you imagine how small these parts are?

An atom has three main parts: *protons, neutrons,* and *electrons.*

Protons and neutrons make up the center of an atom. The center part of an atom is called the *nucleus.*

The electrons are outside the nucleus. They spin around the nucleus at very great speeds. Electrons are much smaller than protons or neutrons.

Protons and electrons have electrical charges.

- Each proton has a *positive* (+) charge.
- Each electron has a *negative* (−) charge.

A neutron is *neutral.* It has *no* charge.

An atom has the same number of protons as electrons.

PROTONS = ELECTRONS

This means that the number of plus charges equals the number of minus charges. They balance each other. Because of this, the entire atom has no charge.

The *atomic number* is also the same as the number of protons.

PROTONS = ATOMIC NUMBER

Three things, then, are equal: the number of protons, the number of electrons, and the atomic number.

P rotons =
E lectrons =
N umber (atomic)

Remember this. If you know any one of these numbers, you know the number of the other two. They are the *same!*

NAME _____

14

UNDERSTANDING THE ATOM

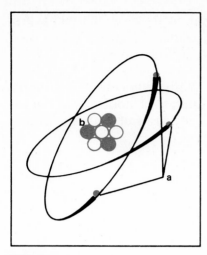

Figure A

Look at Figure A. Answer the questions.

1. The nucleus is labeled _____ .
   <u>a, b</u>

2. The electrons are labeled _____ .
   <u>a, b</u>

3. Name the parts that make up a nucleus.

   _____ _____

4. A proton is _____ than an electron.
   <u>larger, smaller</u>

5. An electron is _____ than a neutron.
   <u>larger, smaller</u>

6. A proton has _____ charge.
   <u>a positive, a negative, no</u>

7. An electron has _____ charge.
   <u>a positive, a negative, no</u>

8. A neutron has _____ charge.
   <u>a positive, a negative, no</u>

9. An entire atom has _____ charge.
   <u>a positive, a negative, no</u>

COMPLETE THE CHART

You will need your Periodic Table to fill in some spaces. (See pages 168–169.)

REMEMBER PEN.

	Name of Element	Symbol	Atomic Number	Number of Protons	Number of Electrons
1.	Oxygen				
2.			20		
3.				53	
4.					11
5.				47	
6.	Sulfur				
7.			80		
8.					26

UNDERSTANDING ATOMIC WEIGHT

Every atom has weight. The weight of an atom is called its *atomic weight.* An atomic weight is not an exact scale reading of weight—like grams or ounces. It is a way of comparing the weight of one atom against the weight of another atom.

The weight of an atom is the weight of its *nucleus.* A nucleus contains protons and neutrons. Therefore the number of protons plus the number of neutrons gives us the atomic weight of an atom. Electrons are so light, that they are not counted in the atomic weight.

- Each proton is given a weight of *one.*

- Each neutron is given a weight of *one.*

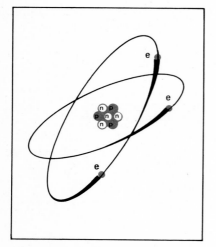

Figure B

For example, a lithium atom has 3 protons and 4 neutrons. The atomic weight of a lithium atom is 7 (3 + 4 = 7).

- Each different kind of atom has its own number of protons.

- Each different kind of atom has its own atomic weight.

Answer these questions.

1. What is the center part of the atom called? _____

2. What parts make up the nucleus? _____ _____

3. The weight of an atom is the weight of its _____ and _____.

4. Fill in the blanks. ATOMIC WEIGHT = _____ + _____

NAME _____

Now fill in the chart.

	Name of Element	Symbol	Number of Protons	Number of Neutrons	Atomic Weight
5.	Neon		10		20
6.	Cobalt		27		59
7.	Gold		79	118	
8.	Chlorine			18	35
9.	Thorium		90	142	
10.	Lead			125	207
11.	Nickel		28		59
12.	Chromium			28	52
13.	Silicon		14		28
14.	Tungsten		74	110	

ROUNDING OFF ATOMIC WEIGHTS

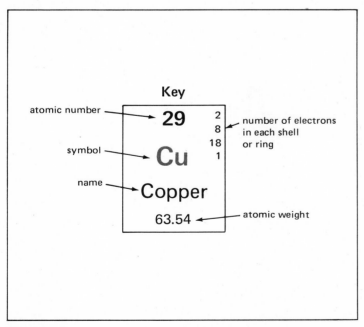

Figure C

This is the "key" to reading the full Periodic Table on pages 168–169.

Copper has been chosen. Any other element could have been chosen.

Notice that the atomic weight of copper is 63.54. This is a whole number followed by two decimals. Most atomic weights have decimals.

In the classroom, we do not use decimals. We round off the decimal to its nearest *whole number*. If the decimal is .5 or greater we round off to the next higher number. If the decimal is less than .5 we round down.

Use this knowledge to fill in the chart. The first two are done as examples.

	Element	Listed Atomic Weight	Rounded-off Atomic Weight
1.	Copper	63.54	64
2.	Calcium	40.08	40
3.	Fluorine	18.99	
4.	Strontium	87.62	
5.	Barium	137.34	
6.	Titanium	47.90	
7.	Magnesium	24.31	
8.	Argon	39.94	
9.	Erbium	167.26	
10.	Zirconium	91.22	

WHAT DO THE PICTURES SHOW?

Figures D and E show atoms. Study each figure and answer the questions about each.

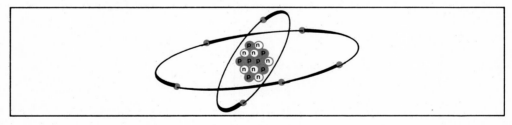

Figure D

1. How many protons does the atom in Figure D have? _____

2. How many neutrons? _____

3. How many electrons? _____

4. What is the atomic weight of this atom? _____

5. What is the name and symbol of this atom? Name _____

   Symbol _____

(Check with your Periodic Table.)

NAME _____

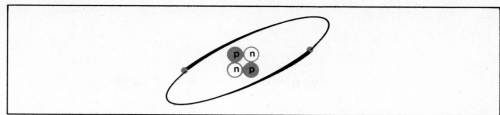

Figure E

6. How many protons does the atom in Figure E have? _____

7. How many neutrons? _____

8. How many electrons? _____

9. What is the atomic weight of this atom? _____

10. What is the name and symbol of this atom?   Name _____

                                                                             Symbol _____

COMPLETING SENTENCES

Complete the sentences with the choices below. Two of these may be used twice. Two of these may be used three times.

plus	no	neutrons
atomic number	atoms	1
circle	electrons	minus
protons		

1. All matter is made up of tiny _____ .

2. The three main parts of an atom are _____, _____, and

    _____ .

3. A nucleus is made up of _____ and _____ .

4. Electrons _____ the nucleus.

5. A proton has a _____ charge; an electron has a _____

charge; a neutron has _____ charge.

6. An entire atom has _____ charge.

7. Protons = electrons = _____ .

8. The atomic weight of an atom is the weight of its _____ and

    _____ .

9. Each proton or neutron is given a weight of _____ .

10. In figuring atomic weight, we do not count the weight of an atom's _____ .

MATCHING Match the two lists. Write the correct letter on the line next to each number.

1. _____ protons and neutrons

   a) no charge

2. _____ electron

   b) add an atom's protons and neutrons

3. _____ proton

   c) make up a nucleus

4. _____ neutron

   d) positive charge

5. _____ to find atomic weight

   e) negative charge

WORD SEARCH The words in this list are hidden within the groups of letters. Try to find each word. When you find it, draw a line around the word. The spelling may go in any direction.

SOLID
LIQUID
GAS
MATTER
COMPOUND
METAL
POSITIVE
FORMULA
SYMBOL

C	F	F	L	I	Q	B	R
P	O	S	I	T	I	V	E
O	R	M	E	T	A	L	T
R	M	D	P	I	L	L	T
A	U	D	I	O	M	O	A
T	L	P	B	U	U	S	M
I	A	M	A	L	Q	N	G
M	Y	B	S	O	L	I	D
S	A	G	E	M	T	A	L

NAME _____

20

HOW ARE ELECTRONS ARRANGED AROUND THE NUCLEUS?

4

shell: rings in which electrons orbit

AIM 4 | How are electrons arranged around the nucleus?

Electrons orbit the nucleus in paths called *rings* or *shells*. Hydrogen and helium have one electron shell. All other atoms have two or more shells.

Each shell is named with a capital letter. The first shell is called the "K" shell. It is closest to the nucleus. The next shell is the "L" shell. The "M" shell comes next. And so on.

Each shell can hold only a certain number of electrons.

The "K" shell can hold 2 electrons.

The "L" shell can hold 8 electrons.

The "M" shell can hold 8 electrons.*

The number of shells an atom has depends upon its number of electrons. Each shell must have its full number of electrons before a new shell starts. If there are more electrons than a shell can hold, a new shell starts.

The outer shell of most electrons is not full. Only the atoms of the elements of Group O have full outer shells.

■ Atoms of *metals* have fewer *than 4 outer-ring electrons*.

■ Atoms of *nonmetals* have more than 4 outer-ring electrons.

---

*through atomic number 20.

NAME _____

WHAT DO THE PICTURES SHOW?

Figures A and B show how electrons are arranged in two atoms. Study each figure. Then answer the questions.

Figure A shows a magnesium atom.

The atomic number of magnesium is 12.

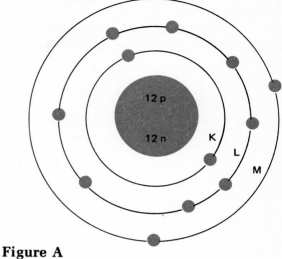

Figure A

1. How many electron shells does magnesium have? _____

2. **a)** What is the first shell called?

   _____

   b) How many electrons does the first shell have? _____

   c) Is the first shell full? _____

   d) The K shell is _____ the nucleus.

   closest to, farthest from

3. **a)** What is the second shell called? _____

   b) Is this the outer shell? _____

   c) How many electrons does the second shell have? _____

   d) Is the second shell full? _____

4. **a)** What is the third shell called? _____

   b) How many electrons does the third shell have? _____

   c) Is the third shell full? _____

   d) Is this the outer shell? _____

5. **a)** Magnesium is a _____.

   metal, nonmetal

   b) Why? _____

6. Find magnesium in the Periodic Table.

   Magnesium is found in Period _____, Group _____.

Figure B shows a sulfur atom.
The atomic number of sulfur is 16.

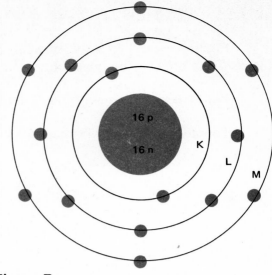

Figure B

7. How many electron shells does sulfur have? _____

8. **a)** What is the first shell called? _____

   b) How many electrons does the first shell have? _____

   c) Is the first shell full? _____

9. **a)** What is the second shell called? _____

   b) Is this the outer shell? _____

   c) How many electrons does the second shell have? _____

   d) Is the second shell full? _____

10. **a)** What is the third shell called? _____

    b) How many electrons does the third shell have? _____

    c) Is the third shell full? _____

    d) Is this the outer shell? _____

11. **a)** Sulfur is a _____.
       _{metal, nonmetal}

    b) Why? _____

12. Find sulfur in the Periodic Table.

    Sulfur is found in Period _____, Group _____.

NAME _____

24

FILL IN THE BLANKS

Write the correct term in each blank to complete the sentence.

1. The first electron shell is the _____ shell. It can hold _____ electrons.

2. The second electron shell is the _____ shell. It can hold _____ electrons.

3. The third electron shell is the _____ shell. It can hold _____ electrons.

4. A metal has _____ than 4 outer-ring electrons.

5. A nonmetal has _____ than 4 outer-ring electrons.

FILL IN THE ELECTRONS

Decide how many electrons each of these atoms in Figures C through F has. Then draw the electrons in their proper shells. Make a small ball • to show an electron. REMEMBER PEN .

Label each shell that is not already labeled. Then answer the questions next to each diagram.

The first exercise has been filled in as an example.

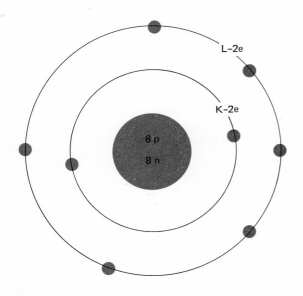

Figure C

Oxygen-atomic number 8

1. How many electrons does oxygen have? _____8_____

2. List the electron shells and the number of electrons in each shell.

   _____K shell—2 electrons_____

   _____L shell—6 electrons_____

3. Is the outer shell complete? _____No_____

4. How many electrons does the outer shell have? _____6_____

5. Oxygen is a ___nonmetal___.
   <u>metal, nonmetal</u>

25

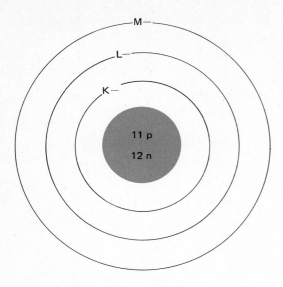

Figure D
Sodium-atomic number 11

6. How many electrons does sodium have? _____

7. List the electron shells and the number of electrons in each shell.

_____

_____

_____

8. Is the outer shell complete?

_____

9. How many electrons does the outer shell have? _____

10. Sodium is a _____.
    metal, nonmetal

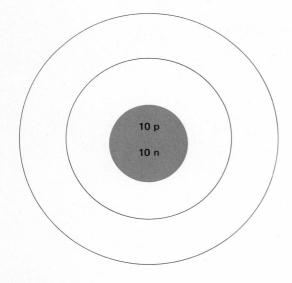

Figure E
Neon-atomic number 10

11. How many electrons does neon have? _____

12. List the electron shells and the number of electrons in each shell.

_____

_____

13. Is the outer shell complete?

_____

14. How many electrons does the outer shell have? _____

15. Neon is a _____.
    metal, nonmetal

NAME _____

26

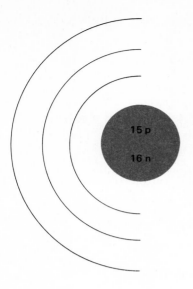

Figure F
Phosphorus—atomic number 15

16. How many electrons does phosphorus have? _____

17. List the electron shells and the number of electrons in each shell.

_____

_____

_____

18. Is the outer shell complete?

_____

19. How many electrons does the outer shell have? _____

20. Phosphorus is a _____.
   metal, nonmetal

COMPLETING SENTENCES Complete the sentences with the choices below. One of these may be used twice.

nucleus	L	Group O
full	rings	K
metals	not	nonmetals
shells	closest	

1. Electrons move around the _____ of an atom.

2. The paths of moving electrons are called _____ or _____.

3. The first electron shell is called the _____ shell.

4. The K shell is the shell that is _____ to the _____.

5. The second electron shell is called the _____ shell.

6. Before a new shell is started, the shell before it must be _____.

7. Most outer electron shells are _____ full.

8. The only atoms that have full outer shells are in _____.

9. Atoms with 1, 2, or 3 outer-ring electrons are _____.

10. Atoms with 5, 6, 7, or 8 outer-ring electrons are _____.

MATCHING Match the two lists. Write the correct letter on the line next to each number.

1. _____ protons and neutrons   **a)** circle the nucleus

2. _____ electrons   **b)** more than 4 outer-ring electrons

3. _____ K, L, M   **c)** make up the nucleus

4. _____ metals   **d)** fewer than 4 outer-ring electrons

5. _____ nonmetals   **e)** first three electron rings

CROSSWORD PUZZLE Fill in the blank spaces by following the clues across and down.

Across

1. The smallest part of an element
4. Long-playing (abbreviation)
6. Matter made up of one kind of atom
9. Food that comes from an animal
10. In a place
11. To operate an automobile
12. Where electrons orbit; also found by the sea
15. First electron ring
16. Morning (abbreviation)
18. To stop living
20. A kind of electric current (abbreviation)
21. A man's name
23. What a flame is; not cold
24. K, L, or M for example

Down

2. Needed for chewing
3. Iron or aluminum for example

4. Second and third electron rings
5. Elements of the same row across
7. The last part
8. Part of your foot
9. Face covering
13. Two for a dollar or fifty cents
    _____
14. Coming after all others
17. Short for mother
19. A bird hatches from one
22. Mister (abbreviation)

HOW DO SOME COMPOUNDS FORM?

5

ion: an atom with a charge

AIM 5 | How do some compounds form?

You have learned about electron shells. Now use this knowledge to understand how atoms link up to form compounds.

Not all atoms form compounds. Only atoms that have outer shells that are *not* full form compounds.

The elements of Group O have complete outer shells. These atoms do *not* form compounds. All other atoms have outer shells that are not full. All other atoms form compounds.

Atoms form compounds by combining their outer-ring electrons. A total of 8 outer-ring electrons is needed.

Here's an example. An atom with 7 outer-ring electrons will form a compound with an atom with 1 outer-ring electron. (7 + 1 = 8.) (See Figure C.)

An atom with 6 outer-ring electrons will link up with an atom with 2 outer-ring electrons. (6 + 2 = 8.)

In Aim 4 you learned that:

■ Atoms of *metals* have *fewer* than 4 outer-ring electrons.

■ Atoms of *nonmetals* have *more* than 4 outer-ring electrons.

When forming a compound:

■ The metal transfers or "lends" outer-ring electrons to the nonmetal.

■ The nonmetal "borrows" these electrons.

Here is an easy way to remember this:

M
E
T
A
LEND > ELECTRONS
S

If metals lend electrons, then nonmetals borrow them. A compound has at least one metal and one nonmetal.

NAME _____

30

UNDERSTANDING HOW A COMPOUND FORMS

Sodium (Na) and chlorine (Cl) link up to form the compound sodium chloride (NaCl)—common table salt. Let's see how it happens.

First, let's look at the *atoms* of sodium and chlorine.

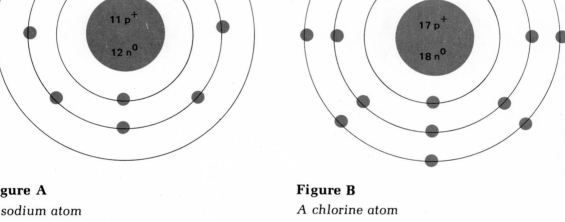

Figure A
A sodium atom

Figure B
A chlorine atom

1. How many protons does a sodium atom have? _____

2. How many electrons? _____

3. Is the number of protons the same as the number of electrons? _____

4. Is a sodium atom neutral?

_____

5. How many outer-ring electrons does sodium have? _____

6. Is its outer ring full? _____

7. Is sodium a metal or a nonmetal?

_____

8. How many protons does a chlorine atom have? _____

9. How many electrons? _____

10. Is the number of protons the same as the number of electrons? _____

11. Is a chlorine atom neutral?

_____

12. How many outer-ring electrons does chlorine have? _____

13. Is its outer ring full? _____

14. Is chlorine a metal or a nonmetal?

_____

15. Which atom will be an electron lender? _____

16. Which atom will be an electron borrower? _____

17. Add up your answers to questions 5 and 12. _____

Is that the same number of electrons that make up a full shell? _____

THE CHEMICAL REACTION

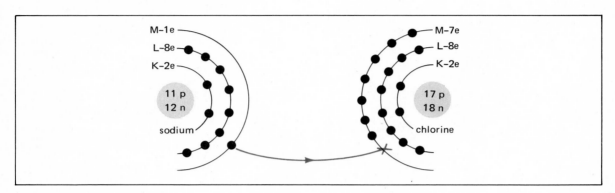

Figure C

1. How many electrons does sodium lose to chlorine? _____

2. Sodium now has _____ electrons and _____ protons.

3. Does sodium still have an equal number of electrons and protons? _____

4. How many electrons does chlorine borrow? _____

5. Chlorine now has _____ electrons and _____ protons.

6. Does chlorine still have an equal number of electrons and protons? _____

When sodium and chlorine combine, sodium LOSES an electron. The chlorine GAINS an electron.

Are sodium and chlorine still neutral atoms? NO! Now, they each have a *charge*.

Sodium has a charge of +1.

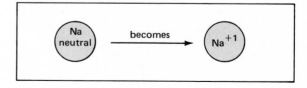

Figure D

NAME _____

Chlorine has a charge of −1.

We know that atoms are *neutral*. Sodium and chlorine are no longer neutral. So they are no longer atoms. They have charges. We call an atom with a charge an ION [EYE on].

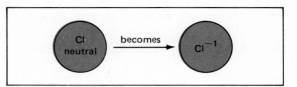

Figure E

Sodium is a *positive* ion because its charge is +1.

Chlorine is a *negative* ion because its charge is −1.

Opposite charges attract. Positive and negative ions are attracted to one another.

The opposite charges hold the sodium and chlorine ions together. Together they form *sodium chloride*. Sodium chloride is a compound.

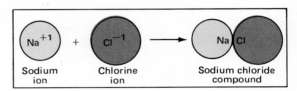

Figure F

LET'S TRY ANOTHER EXAMPLE

Look at Figure G. It shows how one magnesium atom combines with two fluorine atoms.

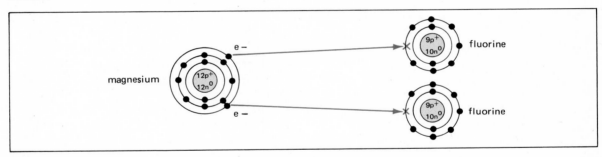

Figure G

1. How many electrons does magnesium lose? _____

2. How many minus charges does magnesium *lose*? _____

3. How many minus charges does magnesium now have? _____

4. How many plus charges does magnesium now have? _____

5. The magnesium now has a _____ charge.
    +2, −2

6. What do we call a charged atom? _____

7. The magnesium is a _____ ion.
    positive, negative

8. How many electrons does *each* fluorine atom gain? _____

9. How many minus charges does *each* fluorine atom gain? _____

10. How many *minus* charges does each fluorine atom now have? _____

11. How many *plus* charges does each fluorine atom now have? _____

12. What charge does each fluorine atom now have? _____

+1, −1

13. The fluorine is now a _____ ion.

positive, negative

14. The magnesium and fluorine ions have _____ charges.

opposite, the same

15. They _____ attract one another.

do, do not

16. The compound that magnesium and fluorine form is magnesium fluoride. What *keeps* the magnesium fluoride together? _____

COMPLETING CHARTS Several elements are listed below. Find them in the Periodic Table (pages 168–169). Then fill in the empty spaces.

The first element, copper, has already been done for you.

	Element	Number of Electrons in Outer Ring	Metal or Nonmetal?	Lends or Borrows Electrons?	Can Lend or Borrow How Many Electrons?
1.	Copper	*1*	*metal*	*lends*	*1*
2.	Phosphorus				
3.	Iodine				
4.	Vanadium				
5.	Cobalt				
6.	Sodium				
7.	Nitrogen				
8.	Helium				
9.	Gold				
10.	Zinc				

NAME _____

MATCHING   Match the two lists. Write the correct letter on the line next to each number.

---

1. _____ compound

2. _____ at least one metal and one nonmetal

3. _____ 8

4. _____ metals

5. _____ nonmetals

a) needed to form a compound

b) borrow electrons

c) two or more linked-up atoms

d) total number of outer-ring electrons needed to form a compound

e) lend electrons

WRITING SYMBOLS FOR IONS

■ An *atom* has no charge. It is shown as a symbol followed by a small zero. For example, this is the symbol for a chlorine atom Cl^0.

■ An *ion* is shown as a symbol followed by the charge value. For example, this is the symbol for a chlorine *ion* Cl^{-1}.

Use what you have learned about atoms and ions. Complete the information below. The first line has been done for you.

ATOMS		IONS
1. Ca^0 − ___*2*___ electrons	$\longrightarrow$	Ca^{+2}
2. O^0 + _____ electrons	$\longrightarrow$	O^{-2}
3. K^0 _____ electron	$\longrightarrow$	K^{+1}
4. Ag^0 _____ electron	$\longrightarrow$	Ag^{+1}
5. F^0 _____ electron	$\longrightarrow$	F^{-1}

NOW LET'S TRY IT ANOTHER WAY.

Again, the first line has been done for you.

ATOMS		IONS
6. Al^0 −3 electrons	$\longrightarrow$	*Al^{+3}*
7. P^0 +3 electrons	$\longrightarrow$	_____
8. Li^0 −1 electron	$\longrightarrow$	_____
9. Be^0 −2 electrons	$\longrightarrow$	_____
10. I^0 +1 electron	$\longrightarrow$	_____

COMPLETING SENTENCES

Complete the sentences with the choices below.

fewer than 4	lend	nonmetal
borrow	2	8
combining	6	more than 4
metal	are not full	

1. A compound has at least _____ atoms linked together.

2. A compound has at least one _____ and one _____.

3. Atoms of metals have _____ outer-ring electrons.

4. Atoms of nonmetals have _____ outer-ring electrons.

5. Only atoms that have outer shells that _____ form compounds.

6. Atoms form compounds by _____ their outer-ring electrons.

7. A compound has a total of _____ outer-ring electrons.

8. Metals _____ electrons.

9. Nonmetals _____ electrons.

10. An atom with 2 outer-ring electrons will form a compound with an atom with

    _____ outer-ring electrons.

THROW ONE OUT

In each of the following sets of terms, one of the terms does *not* belong. Circle that term.

1. proton   electron   plus charge

2. proton   electron   minus charge

3. atom   charge   no charge

4. ion   charge   no charge

5. same charges   opposite charges   attract

REACHING OUT

Turn to your Periodic Table on pages 168–169. One group of atoms does not form ions. Which group is this? _____

NAME _____

WHAT ARE THE PROPERTIES OF METALS?

6

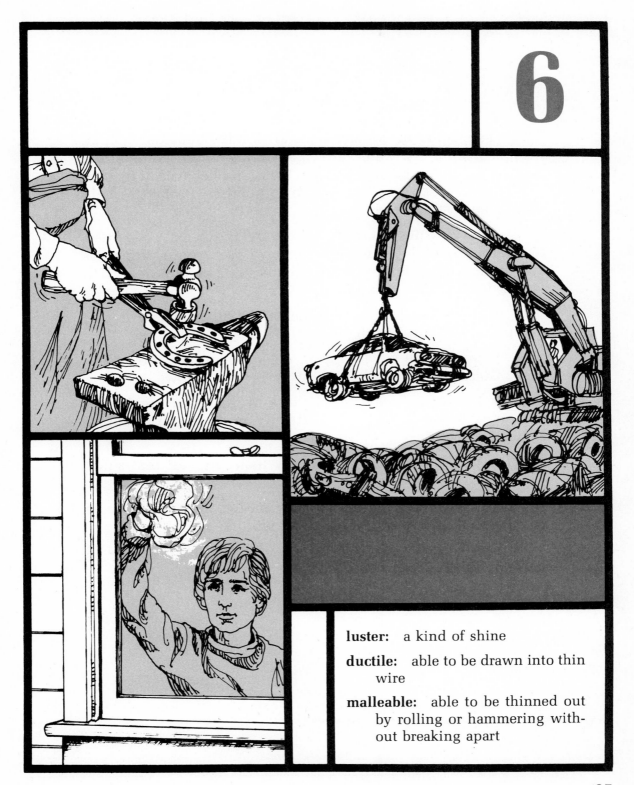

luster: a kind of shine

ductile: able to be drawn into thin wire

malleable: able to be thinned out by rolling or hammering without breaking apart

AIM 6 | What are the properties of metals?

You come in contact with all kinds of matter—paper, plastic, steel, glass, water, air. . . . You have no trouble telling one from another. Each one looks, feels, and behaves in its own special way. Each one has its own properties. Properties help us to identify matter.

No two substances have exactly the same properties. Certain kinds of substances, however, have certain properties that are the same. For example, metals share certain important properties. Let's see what they are.

- Metals are *solid* at room temperature. There is one exception. Mercury is a liquid.

- Metals are *silver-gray in color*. There are two exceptions. Gold and copper are yellow to orange-yellow.

- Metals are *good conductors of heat and electricity.* This means that heat and electricity move easily through metals.

- Metals have a certain shiny look. We call that shine *metallic luster.*

- Metals are *malleable.* This means that they can be hammered or rolled into thin pieces without breaking.

- Metals are also *ductile.* This means that they can be made into thin wires.

NAME _____

38

WHAT DO THE PICTURES SHOW?

Each picture shows a property of metal. Which property is it? Write the correct property under each picture. (Answer in complete sentences.)

Figure A

1. Metals are _____

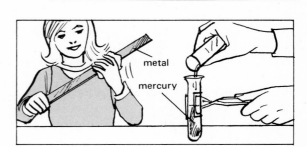

Figure B

2. _____

Figure C

3. _____

Figure D

4. _____

Figure E

5. _____

Figure F

6. _____

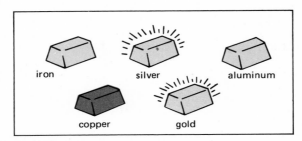

Figure G

7. _____

39

COMPLETING SENTENCES

Complete the sentences with the choices below. Two of these may be used twice.

liquid   nonmetals   copper
ductile   mercury   atoms
silver-gray   gas   the same
solid   share   metals
properties   gold   conductors of electricity

1. All matter is made up of _____.

2. The three states of matter are _____, _____, and
    _____.

3. Matter is grouped as _____ and _____.

4. Matter is identified by certain "clues." We call these clues _____.

5. No two different substances have properties that are all _____.

6. Certain groups of substances do _____ certain properties.

7. Metals belong to the same group of substances because they share some important
    _____.

8. Metals are _____ at room temperature except for _____.

9. Metals are _____ in color except for _____ and
    _____.

10. A lamp cord proves that metals are good _____.
    It also proves that metals are _____.

MATCHING

Match the two lists. Write the correct letter on the line next to each number.

1. _____ metallic luster   a) can be hammered without breaking

2. _____ properties   b) building blocks of matter

3. _____ malleable   c) color of most metals

4. _____ atoms   d) help to identify matter

5. _____ silver-gray   e) special kind of shine

NAME _____

MORE ON PROPERTIES

Look at Figures H, I, and J. Then answer the questions.

The aluminum foil that you use at home was made in a huge machine like the one in Figure H.

Figure H

1. What property do metals have that makes aluminum foil possible? _____

You have read about seven properties of metals. Figures I and J show two more properties. Can you figure out what they are?

Write your answers by completing the sentences below each figure.

Figure I

2. Most metals are _____

Figure J

3. Most metals are _____

TRUE OR FALSE

Write T on the line next to the number if the sentence is true. Write F if the sentence is false.

1. _____ A waxed floor has a shine.

2. _____ A waxed floor has a metallic luster.

3. _____ Mercury is a liquid at room temperature.

4. _____ Mercury is a metal.

5. _____ All metals are solid.

6. _____ Most metals are silver-gray.

7. _____ Only metals are silver-gray.

8. _____ Gold is silver-gray.

9. _____ Wood is ductile.

10. _____ Wood is a metal.

WORD SCRAMBLE

Unscramble each of the following to form a word or term that you have read in this Aim.

1. LEAMT _____

2. RUSTEL _____

3. CLUDITE _____

4. CYMRRUE _____

REACHING OUT

The properties of metals and non-metals are generally *opposite*. Make a list of some of the properties of *non-metals*.

_____

_____

_____

_____

NAME _____

WHAT IS VALENCE?

+

11	2 8 1
Na	
Sodium	
22.9898	

−

35	2 8 18 7
Br	
Bromine	
79.909	

BANK 1902

LOANS
UP TO
$5,000.

valence: the ability of an atom to lend or borrow electrons

AIM 7 | What is valence?

Atoms of metals link up with atoms of nonmetals. They form compounds. When a compound forms, the metal lends outer-ring electrons to the nonmetal. The nonmetal borrows the electrons.

How many electrons does an atom lend or borrow? It depends upon the atom. It also depends upon the compound being formed. Some atoms give up or take on more electrons than others. The number of electrons an atom can lend or borrow is called its *valence.*

A valence is a number with a plus (+) or minus (−) sign in front of it. The valence is written next to the atom it describes, such as Al^{+3}, Mg^{+2}, Br^{-1}, and Se^{-2}.

The *sign* (+ or −) tells us whether the atom lends or borrows electrons.

A plus (+) sign means that the atom *lends* electrons.

A minus (−) sign means that the atom *borrows* electrons.

The *number* tells us *how many* electrons the atom lends or borrows.

Let's look at two valences.

■ Sodium has a valence of +1 (Na^{+1}). This means that sodium can *lend one electron.*

■ The valence of oxygen is −2 (O^{-2}). Oxygen can *borrow two electrons.*

Metals have *plus* valences. Metals *lend* electrons.

Nonmetals have *minus* valences. Nonmetals *borrow* electrons.

A nonmetal will borrow enough electrons to complete its outer shell.

Many elements have more than one valence. In fact, some elements have both plus *and* minus valences. Sometimes they lend electrons. Sometimes they borrow.

NAME _____

USING THE PERIODIC TABLE TO FIND VALENCE

You can find the valence of many elements by looking at the Periodic Table (pages 168–169).

Finding the Valence of a Metal

This is the simplest valence to find. In many cases, the valence of a metal is the same as the number of electrons in its outer shell.

A metal *lends* (loses) electrons. Therefore, its valence is *plus* (+).

Figure A shows an example.

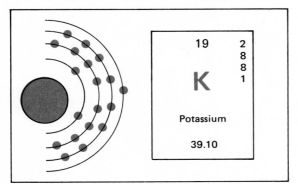

19	2
	8
	8
K	1
Potassium	
39.10	

Potassium has *1* outer-shell electron.

Potassium lends this single electron.

The valence of potassium is +*1* (K^{+1}).

Figure A

Finding the Valence of a Nonmetal

This is simple too. Here is what to do:

■ Check the number of electrons in the outer shell.

■ Figure out how many electrons that atom needs to make a complete outer shell (8 electrons). *That* number is the valence number.

A nonmetal will add (borrow) these electrons. Therefore, its valence is minus (−).

Figure B shows an example.

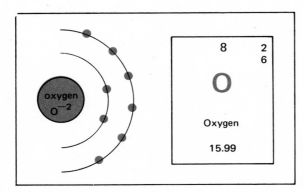

8	2
	6
O	
Oxygen	
15.99	

Oxygen has 6 outer-shell electrons.

Oxygen needs 2 more electrons to fill its outer shell ($8 - 6 = 2$).

Oxygen will borrow (gain) these 2 electrons.

The valence of oxygen is $^{-2}$ (O^{-2}).

Figure B

Now try these yourself

4	2
	2

Be

Beryllium
9.01

Figure C

1. How many outer-shell electrons does beryllium have? _____

2. Beryllium is a _____ .
   <small>metal, nonmetal</small>

3. Beryllium _____ electrons.
   <small>lends, borrows</small>

4. How many electrons can beryllium lend? _____

5. What is the valence of beryllium? _____

6. **a)** How many outer-shell electrons does sulfur have? _____

   b) Is this a full shell? _____

   c) How many electrons are needed to make a full shell?

   _____

16	2
	8
	6

S

Sulfur

32.06

Figure D

7. Sulfur is a _____ .
   <small>metal, nonmetal</small>

8. Sulfur _____ electrons.
   <small>lends, borrows</small>

9. How many electrons can sulfur borrow? _____

10. What is the valence of sulfur? _____

11. **a)** How many outer-shell electrons does iodine have? _____

    b) Is this a full shell? _____

    c) How many electrons will make it a full shell? _____

53	2
	8
	18
	18
	7

I

Iodine

126.90

Figure E

12. Iodine is a _____ .
    <small>metal, nonmetal</small>

13. Iodine _____ electrons.
    <small>loses, gains</small>

14. How many electrons can iodine gain? _____

15. What is the valence of iodine? _____

NAME _____

46

COMPLETING SENTENCES

Complete the sentences with the choices below.

lend　　　　　　　lends or borrows　　　　number
more than one　　 borrow　　　　　　　outer shell
how many　　　　 loses　　　　　　　　compounds
eight　　　　　　　+ or − sign　　　　　 gains
valence

1. Metals link up with nonmetals to form _____.

2. When forming compounds, metals _____ electrons. Nonmetals _____ electrons.

3. The ability of an atom to lend or borrow electrons is called its _____.

4. A valence is written as a _____ followed by a _____.

5. The *number* tells us _____ electrons an atom gains or loses.

6. The *sign* tells us whether the atom _____ electrons.

7. An atom with a plus (+) valence lends electrons. Another way of saying that is: An atom with a plus valence _____ electrons.

8. An atom with a minus (−) valence borrows electrons. Another way of saying this is: An atom with a minus valence _____ electrons.

9. A nonmetal will borrow enough electrons to complete its _____. A complete outer shell usually has _____ electrons.

10. Many elements have _____ valence.

MATCHING

Match the two lists. Write the correct letter on the line next to each number.

1. _____ compound

2. _____ a total of 8 outer-shell electrons

3. _____ valence

4. _____ + valence atom

5. _____ − valence atom

a) an atom's combining ability

b) lends electrons

c) at least one metal and one nonmetal

d) borrows electrons

e) needed to form a compound

WORKING WITH VALENCES

Ten elements and their valences are listed below. Study each one. Then fill in the chart. The first line has been filled in for you.

	Element	Symbol and valence number	Metal or nonmetal	Lends or borrow electrons?	Lends or borrows how many electrons?
1.	Oxygen	O^{-2}	*Nonmetal*	*borrows*	*2*
2.	Calcium	Ca^{+2}			
3.	Aluminum	Al^{+3}			
4.	Bromine	Br^{-1}			
5.	Nitrogen	N^{-3}			
6.	Zinc	Zn^{+2}			
7.	Lithium	Li^{+1}			
8.	Sulfur	S^{-2}			
9.	Phosphorus	P^{-3}			
10.	Silver	Ag^{+1}			

TRUE OR FALSE Write T on the line next to the number if the sentence is true Write F if the sentence is false.

1. _____ Valence is the number of electrons an atom has.

2. _____ Every element has the same valence.

3. _____ Some elements have more than one valence.

4. _____ An atom with a plus (+) valence lends electrons.

5. _____ An atom with a minus (−) valence borrows electrons.

6. _____ An atom with a +2 valence can borrow two electrons.

7. _____ An atom with a valence of +2 can lend two electrons.

8. _____ An atom with 6 outer-ring electrons can lend 3 electrons.

9. _____ An atom with 7 outer-ring electrons has a valence of −1.

10. _____ An atom with 7 outer-ring electrons can borrow 1 electron.

NAME _____

48

HOW CAN VALENCE HELP US TO WRITE FORMULAS?

AIM 8 | How can valence help us to write formulas?

There are millions of compounds. Each one has its own formula. No two compounds have the same formula.

Many formulas are very complicated. For example, the formula for a certain substance in your blood is $C_{3032}H_{4816}O_{872}N_{780}S_8F_4$. *This* is a complicated formula for a complicated molecule.

Many formulas, however, are very simple—like H_2O. Most people know that H_2O is the formula for water. Water contains only two kinds of atoms.

You can figure out the formula for any simple compound. All you need to know are the symbols and the valences of the elements that make up the compound. JUST CRISS-CROSS THE VALENCE NUMBERS.

This is how to write the formula for water:

Water is made up of hydrogen (H) and oxygen (O). The valence of hydrogen is +1 (H^{+1}). The valence of oxygen is −2 (O^{-2}).

Step 1 Write down the *symbol* of each element. List the + valence element first.

H O

Step 2 Mark down the *valence* of each element next to the element like this:

$$H^{+1}O^{-2}$$

Step 3 *Criss-cross* the valence numbers *only*. Leave out the signs.

$$H^{+1}O^{-2}$$
$$H_2 O_1 = H_2O_1$$

One molecule of water, then, contains 2 atoms of hydrogen and 1 atom of oxygen.

In a final formula, we do not write any 1's. So the formula for water is H_2O.

NAME _____

USING VALENCES TO FIND FORMULAS

Example #1

Table salt is made up of atoms of sodium (Na) and chlorine (Cl).

The valence of sodium is $^{+1}$ (Na^{+1}).

The valence of chlorine is $^{-1}$ (Cl^{-1}).

Write it down. $Na^{+1}Cl^{-1}$

Cross over the signs. $\begin{array}{c} Na^{+1}Cl^{-1} \\ Na_1 \quad Cl_1 \end{array}$

Cancel out the numbers. Na_1Cl_1

The formula for table salt is **NaCl.**

Table salt is *sodium chloride.* One molecule of sodium chloride has 1 atom of sodium and 1 atom of chlorine. Altogether one molecule of salt contains 2 atoms.

Example #2

What do you do if *both* valence *numbers* (not the signs) are the same? This is the case when magnesium and oxygen combine.

$$\begin{array}{c} Mg^{+2}O^{-2} \\ Mg_2 \quad O_2 \quad = Mg_2O_2 \end{array}$$

In some compounds, the numbers are left alone. *But,* not in the compounds you will work with.

If you run across a case like this, cancel out *both* numbers like this: Mg_2O_2.

The formula, then is **MgO.**

WRITING FORMULAS

Work these out by yourself. It's easy! Just do one step at a time.

Example A

Calcium (Ca) links up with iodine (I) to form a compound called *calcium iodide.*

- The valence of calcium is +2 (Ca^{+2}).

- The valence of iodine is −1 (I^{-1}).

1. Write down each element and its valence. (Remember, the + valence comes first.)

1. [ ]

2. Cross over the signs.

2. [ ]

3. Cancel out numbers. (Skip if not needed.)

3. [ ]

4. Write the formula.

4. [ ]

5. What is the *name* of this compound? _____

6. One molecule of calcium iodide has _____ atom(s) of calcium and _____ atom(s) of iodine.

7. Altogether, how many atoms does one molecule of calcium iodide have? _____

Example B

Gold and sulfur combine to form the compound *gold sulfide*.

- The valence of gold is +1 (Au^{+1}).

- The valence of sulfur is −2 (S^{-2}).

8. Write down each element and its valence.

8. [ ]

9. Cross over signs.

9. [ ]

10. Cancel out numbers. (Skip if not needed.)

10. [ ]

11. Write the formula.

11. [ ]

12. What is the name of this compound? _____

13. One molecule of gold sulfide has _____ atom(s) of gold and _____ atom(s) of sulfur.

14. Altogether, how many atoms does one molecule of gold sulfide have? _____

NAME _____

52

Example C

Iron (Fe) and oxygen (O) form a compound called *iron oxide.* You call it *rust.*

- The valence of iron in this compound is +3. (Fe^{+3}).

- The valence of oxygen is −2 (O^{-2}).

15. Write down each element and its valence.

15. [ ]

16. Cross over signs.

16. [ ]

17. Cancel out numbers. (Skip if not needed.)

17. [ ]

18. Write the formula.

18. [ ]

19. **a)** What is the *chemical* name of this compound? _____

b) What is its *common* name? _____

20. One molecule of iron oxide has _____ atom(s) of iron, and

_____ atom(s) of oxygen.

21. Altogether, how many atoms does one atom of iron oxide have? _____

FILL IN THE CHART

Write the correct formulas in the spaces below. Three formulas have been written for you.

NONMETALS

		Cl^{-1}	S^{-2}	O^{-2}	I^{-1}	Br^{-1}
	H^{+1}	1. *HCl*	2.	3. *H_2O*	4.	5.
	Al^{+3}	6.	7.	8.	9. *AlI_3*	10.
METALS	Ca^{+2}	11.	12.	13.	14.	15.
	Cu^{+1}	16.	17.	18.	19.	20.
	Mg^{+2}	21.	22.	23.	24.	25.
	Na^{+1}	26.	27.	28.	29.	30.

REACHING OUT

Valence can help you to find a formula. It goes the other way too.

A FORMULA CAN HELP YOU FIND THE VALENCES OF THE ELEMENTS IN A COMPOUND.

Example: NiI_2 is the formula for nickel iodide. The formula tells us that:

■ The valence of nickel is +2. (Remember, the metal always goes first—and a metal has a positive (+) valence.)

■ The valence of iodine is −1.

Six compounds are listed below. Figure out the valence of the elements in each compound. The first one has been done for you.

	Formula	Atoms and Their Valences	
1.	CaF_2	Ca^{+2}	F^{-1}
2.	KBr		
3.	Mg_3N_2		
4.	CCl_4		
5.	H_2S		
6.	$FeCl_3$		

SPELL THE MISSING WORD

Fill in the missing letters to spell the terms that fit the definitions.

When you have answered correctly, you will spell another term in the box.

1. ___ v ___ | ___ l ___ n ___ e ___
2. ___ e ___ | ___ a ___ ___
3. ___ l ___ | ___ s ___
4. ___ | ___ i ___ ___ u ___

1. the number of electrons an atom lends or borrows
2. elements that lend electrons
3. *not* gain
4. opposite of plus

NAME _____

WHAT IS A RADICAL?

9

OH

(OH)

radical: a group of atoms that acts
        as a single atom

AIM 9 | What is a radical?

Many friends are "extra" good friends. They get together very often. And then, they seem to act like *one* person.

Certain elements are like that. They "get together" whenever possible. And then, they act as if they were *one* element.

A group of atoms that behaves like a *single* atom is called a *radical.* A radical has its *own* valence.

Eight common radicals along with their valences are listed on the facing page. All the common radicals have a *minus* valence except one. The *ammonium* radical (NH_4) has a $+1$ valence $(NH_4)^{+1}$.

The radicals in the chart are listed within parenthesis like (OH). A parenthesis is not always needed. For example, the (OH) in the formula $Na(OH)$ does not need a parenthesis. It can be written as $NaOH$.

A parenthesis is always needed when a *subscript* follows a radical. Take this formula for example—$Ca(OH)_2$. The small 2 after the OH is a *subscript.* It means that one molecule of this compound has two *hydroxyl* (OH) radicals.

How do you find the formula for a simple compound that has one or even *two* radicals? It's simple. *Just criss-cross the valences*—just as you did in Aim 8.

Here are two examples.

1. $Ca_2 + (CO_3)^{-2}$

    $Ca_2(CO_3)_2$ (cancel out the 2's)

The final formula is $Ca(CO_3)$ or $CaCO_3$. Either one may be used. The name for this compound is *calcium carbonate.*

2. $(NH_4)^{+1} + (PO_4)^{-3}$

    $(NH_4)_3(PO_4)_1$ (cancel out the 1)

The final formula is $(NH_4)_3PO_4$. The name for this compound is *ammonium phosphate.*

UNDERSTANDING RADICALS

Chart I shows eight common radicals.

Radical	Formula and Valence
Ammonium	$(NH_4)^{+1}$
Bicarbonate	$(HCO_3)^{-1}$
Hydroxyl	$(OH)^{-1}$
Nitrate	$(NO_3)^{-1}$

Radical	Formula and Valence
Carbonate	$(CO_3)^{-2}$
Sulfite	$(SO_3)^{-2}$
Sulfate	$(SO_4)^{-2}$
Phosphate	$(PO_4)^{-3}$

Chart I

Now look at Chart II. The names of the eight radicals are listed in column A.

Do the following:

In Column B, write the formula of each radical.
In Column C, list the elements that make up each radical and the number of atoms of each element.
In Column D, list the valence of each radical.

The first one has been completed for you.

A Radical Name	B Formula (Don't list the valence here.)	C Elements and Number of Atoms of Each	D Valence
1. Sulfate	*SO₄*	*Sulfur—1 atom* *Oxygen—4 atoms*	*−2*
2. Bicarbonate			
3. Nitrate			
4. Ammonium			
5. Phosphate			
6. Carbonate			
7. Hydroxyl			
8. Sulfite			

Chart II

NAMING COMPOUNDS

Eight compounds are listed in Chart III. Each one contains at least one radical. Name each compound. Choose from the list below.

NOTE: In a compound, the hydroxyl radical (OH) is called *hydroxide*.

calcium carbonate   sodium sulfate
ammonium nitrate   ammonium chloride
potassium hydroxide   silver nitrate
copper nitrate   ammonium hydroxide

	Formula	Name
1.	$Ag(NO_3)$	
2.	$K(OH)$	
3.	NH_4Cl	
4.	$Ca(CO_3)$	
5.	$Cu(NO_3)_2$	
6.	$NH_4(OH)$	
7.	$NH_4(NO_3)$	
8.	$Na_2(SO_4)$	

Chart III

WRITING FORMULAS

Write the correct formulas on Chart IV. Two formulas have been written for you.

Remember: The plus valence goes first. Then criss-cross the valences.

For example: $K^{+1} + (PO_4)^{-3}$

      $K_3(PO_4)_1$

	$(OH)^{-1}$	$(NO_3)^{-1}$	$(PO_4)^{-3}$	$(HCO_3)^{-1}$	$(SO_4)^{-2}$
K^{+1}	1.	2.	3. $K_3(PO_4)$	4.	5.
Mg^{+2}	6.	7. $Mg(NO_3)_2$	8.	9.	10.
H^{+1}	11.	12.	13.	14.	15.

Chart IV

NAME _____

WHAT IS A POLYVALENT ELEMENT?

10

"FERROUS"

"POLY"

polyvalent: having more than one valence

AIM 10 | What is a polyvalent element?

"Poly" means *many* or *more than one*. "Valent" means having to do with valence. *Polyvalent*, then, means having more than one valence.

Many elements are polyvalent. They have more than one valence. *Iron* (Fe), for example, has a valence of +2 (Fe^{+2}). Iron can also have a valence of +3 (Fe^{+3}).

Mercury (Hg), has a valence of +1 (Hg^{+1}). Mercury can also have a valence of +2 (Hg^{+2}).

A polyvalent metal can form more than one kind of compound with the same nonmetal.

For example, iron (Fe) combines with chlorine (Cl^{-1}). The compound that forms can be *either* $FeCl_2$ or $FeCl_3$. Which one? It depends upon the valence of the iron.

If +2 valence iron (Fe^{+2}) takes part in the reaction we get $FeCl_2$.

$FeCl_2$ is called FERROUS chloride. The *ferr-* part comes from *ferre*, the Latin word for iron. The *-ous* ending tells us that the *lower* valence of iron took part in the reaction.

Ferrous chloride is also called *iron II chloride*. The Roman numeral tells us the valence of a polyvalent metal. Iron II means that the valence of iron in ferrous chloride is +2.

If +3 valence iron takes place in the reaction we get $FeCl_3$.

$FeCl_3$ is called FERRIC chloride. The *-ic* ending tells us that the *higher* valence iron took part in the reaction.

Ferric chloride is also called *iron III chloride*. What does iron III mean?

NAME _____

WORKING WITH POLYVALENT ELEMENTS

Chart I shows five elements that are polyvalent. It shows the different valences and the names that their compounds have.

VALENCES OF METALS

Metal	Lower Valence	Name	Higher Valence	Name
Iron	Fe^{+2}	ferrous	Fe^{+3}	ferric
Mercury	Hg^{+1}	mercurous	Hg^{+2}	mercuric
Copper	Cu^{+1}	cuprous	Cu^{+2}	cupric
Gold	Au^{+1}	aurous	Au^{+3}	auric
Tin	Sn^{+2}	stannous	Sn^{+4}	stannic

Chart I

Use Chart I and what you have read to do these exercises.

1. How many valences does each of these elements have? _____

2. The name of each *lower* valence compound ends with _____.

-ous, -ic

3. The name of each *higher* valence compound ends with _____.

-ous, -ic

In a compound, "ferr-" means *iron*. Which elements do these stand for?

4. stann-_____   5. cupr-_____   6. aur-_____

Write the symbols and valences on Chart II. The first one has been done for you.

		Symbol	Valences	
7.	Iron	*Fe*	*+2*	*+3*
8.	Tin			
9.	Gold			
10.	Mercury			
11.	Copper			

Chart II

WRITING FORMULAS

Write the formula for each combination. Then answer the questions. The first one has been done for you.

1. a) $Fe^{+2} + I^{-1} \longrightarrow$

    $$Fe I_2$$

    Circle the correct answer.

    b) The name of this compound is (ferrous) iodide.
       ferric

    c) Another name for this compound is *iron II* iodide.

2. a) $Hg^{+2} + Br^{-1} \longrightarrow$

    b) The name of this compound is mercurous bromide.
       mercuric

    c) Another name for this compound is _____ bromide.

3. a) $Sn^{+2} + F^{-1} \longrightarrow$

    b) The name of this compound is stannous fluoride.
       stannic

    c) Another name for this compound is _____.

4. a) $Cu^{+1} + S^{-2} \longrightarrow$

    b) The name of this compound is cuprous sulfide.
       cupric

    c) Another name for this compound is _____ sulfide.

REACHING OUT

Which compound on this page is found in a familiar household product?

_____

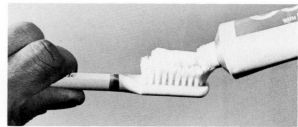

Figure A

NAME _____

WHAT IS FORMULA WEIGHT?

$$\overset{23}{Na}\overset{35}{Cl} = 58$$

11

$C_{12} H_{22} O_{11}$

PURE CANE Sugar GRANULATED PURE CANE Sugar

NET WT. 5 LBS. 2.27 KILOGRAMS

SALT NET WT. 742.9 GRAMS (26 OZ.)

formula weight: the weight of one molecule of a compound; also called molecular weight

AIM 11 | What is formula weight?

Every compound has a formula. For example, H_2O is the formula for water. NaCl is the formula for table salt. $C_{12}H_{22}O_{11}$ is the formula for table sugar.

Compounds are made of atoms. Atoms have weight. Therefore, compounds have weight.

If we add the weight of all the atoms in a compound, we find the weight of one molecule of that compound.

The weight of one molecule of a compound is called its *formula weight*. It is also called its *molecular weight*.

Let's look at an example.

How to find the formula weight of ferric oxide (Fe_2O_3):

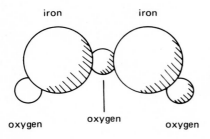

iron   iron

oxygen   oxygen   oxygen

One molecule of ferric oxide (Fe_2O_3) has 2 atoms of iron and 3 atoms of oxygen.

Element	Number of atoms	Atomic weight rounded off (Weight of one atom)	Total weight of atoms
Iron	2	× 56	112
Oxygen	3	× 16	48
			160 =
			FORMULA WEIGHT (Weight of one molecule of Fe_2O_3)

WORKING WITH FORMULA WEIGHTS

Find the formula (molecular) weight of each compound that follows. Look up the symbol names and atomic weights. (You probably know the names of most of these symbols.)

1. Sulfuric acid H_2SO_4

Element	Number of atoms	Atomic weight	Total weight of atoms
Hydrogen	2	×	
Sulfur	1	×	
Oxygen	4	×	

Chart I   Formula weight = _____

2. Sucrose (table sugar) $C_{12}H_{22}O_{11}$

Element	Number of atoms	Atomic weight	Total weight of atoms

Chart II   Formula weight = _____

3. Sodium bicarbonate (baking soda) $NaHCO_3$

Element	Number of atoms	Atomic weight	Total weight of atoms

Chart III   Formula weight = _____

THE INSIDE STORY

Now let's try slightly more difficult compounds. (You will find that they aren't *really* more difficult.)

How do you handle a compound where part of the compound is in *parentheses* and this part is followed by a *subscript*? $Ca(NO_3)_2$ (calcium nitrate) is an example.

Step 1 Find the number of atoms of each element.

$$Ca(NO_3)_2$$

The calcium, Ca, is *outside* the parentheses. No special figuring is needed.

This formula has *one atom of calcium.*

Ca = 1 atom

The nitrate $(NO_3)_2$ needs some very easy figuring.

Simply multiply the *number* of atoms of each element *within* the parentheses by the subscript $(_2)$.

So we have

Subscript

N = 1 × 2 = 2 atoms
O = 3 × 2 = 6 atoms

Step 2 Now we can find the formula weight.

Element	Number of atoms	Atomic weight	Total weight of atoms
Calcium	1	40	40
Nitrogen	2	14	28
Oxygen	6	16	96

Chart IV

164
Formula Weight of
one molecule of $Ca(NO_3)_2$

WORKING WITH COMPOUNDS WITH PARENTHESES

Four formulas are given. Figure out the number of atoms of each element.

1. $Fe(NO_3)_2$ Fe _____

    N _____

    O _____

2. $Al_2(SO_4)_3$ Al _____

    S _____

    O _____

NAME _____

3. $Ba(OH)_2$ Ba _____

O _____

H _____

4. $(NH_4)_2SiF_6$ N _____

H _____

Si _____

F _____

Now that you know how to handle parentheses and subscripts, figure out the formula weight of each formula listed below.

Find the names of the elements in the Periodic Table (pages 168–169).

5. $Ca(OH)_2$

Element	Number of atoms	Atomic weight	Total weight of atoms
Calcium	1		
Oxygen	2		
Hydrogen	2		

Chart V   Formula Weight = _____

6. $Hg_2(SCN)_2$ (S, C, and N are *separate* elements. Naturally! Each one is a capital letter.)

Element	Number of atoms	Atomic weight	Total weight of atoms

Chart VI   Formula weight = _____

7. $Mg(C_7H_5O_3)_2$

Element	Number of atoms	Atomic weight	Total weight of atoms

Chart VII   Formula weight = _____

WHAT DOES THE LARGE NUMBER MEAN?

Sometimes you see a compound or a symbol that has a large number in front of it. What does this mean?

What does the 2 mean in 2Na or 2NaCl? What does the 3 mean in $3H_2$?

The large number tells you to *multiply* each kind of atom by that number. Let's look at some examples:

2Na	2 Na means 2 atoms of sodium.
2NaCl	2NaCl means two molecules of NaCl. That means two atoms of sodium and two atoms of chlorine.
$3H_2$	Here we must *multiply* the **3** × 2. There are 6 atoms of hydrogen.
$3H_2O$	There are still 6 atoms of hydrogen. But we also have oxygen. **3** × 1 = 3 atoms of oxygen.

Now let's see how to handle a compound that has both parentheses and a large number.

$2Ca(NO_3)_2$	The **2** means two molecules of $Ca(NO_3)_2$.

How many atoms of each element does this mean? We must multiply the number of each kind of atom by **2**.

Ca   1 × **2** = 2 atoms

N   1   ×   ②   ×   ②   =   4 atoms

from parentheses	from large number

O   3   ×   ②   ×   ②   =   12 atoms

An important thing to remember!

A large number in front of an element or a compound goes *only* with that element or compound. A plus sign (+) or an arrow → tells us where the value of the large number ends. For example:

$$4Fe + 3O_2 \rightarrow 2Fe_2O_3$$

■ The 4 in front of the Fe goes only with the Fe.

■ The 3 in front of the O_2 goes only with the O_2.

■ But the 2 in front of Fe_2O_3 goes with the Fe_2 and the O_3. They are part of the same molecule.

NAME _____

LET'S JUST COUNT

Count the number of atoms in each of the following:

1. $2Ba(OH)_2$ Ba _____

O _____

H _____

2. $4Al_2(SO_4)_3$ Al _____

S _____

O _____

3. $3Ba(OH)_2$ Ba _____

O _____

H _____

4. $2Mg(C_7H_5O_3)_2$ Mg _____

C _____

H _____

O _____

NOW BACK TO WEIGHTS

Now you know how to handle formulas that have both parentheses and large numbers in front. How do we figure weights for these formulas?

Simple! On page 66 you learned that the formula weight of $Ca(NO_3)_2$ is 164. This means that one molecule weighs 164.

What is the weight of $2Ca(NO_3)_2$? Easy! Just multiply the formula weight by 2.

Weight of $2Ca(NO_3)_2$: $2 \times 164 =$ 328
formula weight

The formula weight of $Ba(OH)_2$ is 171.

Figure the weight of each of the following:

1. $2Ba(OH)_2$ _____

2. $3Ba(OH)_2$ _____

The formula weight of $Pb(NO_3)_2$ is 331.

Figure the weight of each of the following:

3. $2Pb(NO_3)_2$ _____

4. $4Pb(NO_3)_2$ _____

REACHING OUT

1. Find the formula weight of this compound: $Fe(NH_4)_2 (SO_4)_2$.

   _____

2. Find the weight of the following: $2Al_2(SO_3)_3$

   _____

FIND THE DATE Use your knowledge of atomic weights and simple math to find an important date in history.

_____

Step 1 Find the weight of 4 atoms of platinum (Pt).   _____

Step 2 Find the weight of 3 atoms of uranium (U).   _____

Step 3 Add Steps 1 and 2.   _____

Step 4 Find the weight of 2 atoms of hydrogen (H).   _____

Step 5 Subtract Step 4 from Step 3.   _____

What event took place during the year you have written for Step 5?   _____

_____

WHAT IS A CHEMICAL EQUATION?

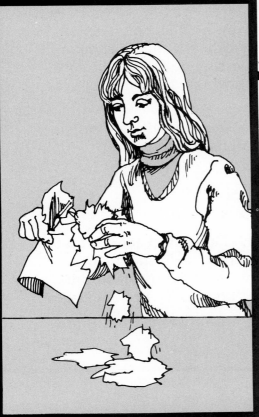

physical change: a change in matter that does not produce any new products

chemical change: a change in matter that produces new products

chemical equation: a set of symbols and formulas that describe a chemical change

reactant: a substance that takes part in a chemical reaction (change)

product: a substance that is produced in a chemical reaction (change)

AIM 12 | What is a chemical equation?

You may tear a sheet of paper into tiny pieces, but you still have paper. Each piece is still paper no matter how small. The way the atoms are linked together has not changed. No new products have been formed. The properties of the paper have not changed. Neither has its formula.

A change like tearing paper is called a *physical* change. In a physical change, only the appearance of a substance changes. The chemical makeup does *not* change.

What happens when you *burn* paper? You no longer have paper. Paper is a compound made up mostly of carbon and hydrogen. When paper burns, it links up with oxygen from the air. Three products form—ash, water, and carbon dioxide. When paper burns, there is a change in the way atoms link together. New products form. Properties change.

A change like burning paper is called a *chemical* change. In a chemical change, the chemical makeup of a substance changes. New products form. Each product has its own properties. Each one has its own formula.

A chemical change is caused by a *chemical reaction.* The "story" of a chemical reaction is called a *chemical equation*. A chemical equation shows two things: (1) which substance(s) we start out with and (2) which substance(s) we end up with.

The substance or substances we start out with are called the *reactants*. The substance or substances we end up with are called the *products*.

This is an example of a chemical equation:

$$Fe + S \longrightarrow FeS$$

This equation describes the chemical reaction that takes place when a mixture of iron (Fe) and sulfur (S) are heated. The Fe and S are the *reactants*. The FeS (iron sulfide) is the *product*. The arrow means "produces" or "yields."

The properties of iron sulfide are different from those of iron or sulfur.

NAME _____

UNDERSTANDING CHEMICAL EQUATIONS

Example 1

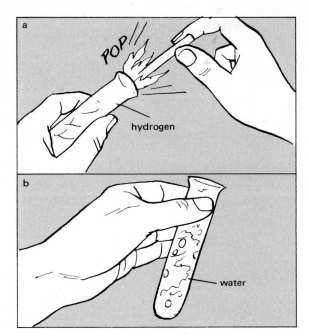

Hydrogen can explode.

When hydrogen explodes it links up with oxygen to form water.

The equation below tells the story of this chemical equation.

$$2H_2 + O_2 \longrightarrow 2H_2O$$

Figure A

Study the equation. Then answer these questions.

1. This formula has two *reactants*. Name them. _____

   _____

2. The reactants are _____ .

elements, compounds

3. This formula has one *product*. Name that product. _____

4. The product is _____ .

an element, a compound

5. Name the states of matter. _____ _____

   _____

6. What is the state of hydrogen? _____

7. What is the state of oxygen? _____

8. What is the state of water? _____

9. Are the properties of hydrogen the same as the properties of water? _____

10. Are the properties of oxygen the same as the properties of water? _____

11. In a chemical reaction, properties _____ change.

do, do not

73

12. a) Name the *kinds* of atoms on the reactant side of this equation. _____

_____

b) Name the *kinds* of atoms on the product side. _____

_____

13. a) The kinds of atoms on the reactant side _____ the same as the
kinds of atoms on the product side.   <u>are, are not</u>

b) Are they in the same form? _____

c) How are they different? Reactant side _____

Product side _____

14. The link-up of the atoms _____ changed.
<u>has, has not</u>

15. In this reaction, atoms have _____.
<u>separated, linked up</u>

16. In a chemical reaction, the link-up of the elements _____ change.
<u>does, does not</u>

17. a) In a chemical equation, the reactants are on the _____ of the
arrow.   <u>right, left</u>

b) The products are on the _____.
<u>right, left</u>

Example 2

Figure B

   Table salt (NaCl) is a white solid.
Your body contains this salt. It is neces-
sary for life.

Figure C

   Sodium (Na) is a very dangerous
solid. It can explode in water.

   Swallowing sodium can cause
death.

NAME _____

Figure D

Chlorine (Cl) is a deadly greenish-yellow gas. If you inhale enough of this gas, you will die.

Table salt can be melted. If an electric current passes through melted sodium chloride, a chemical reaction takes place. This the chemical equation for this reaction.

$$2NaCl \longrightarrow 2Na + Cl_2$$

Study the equation. Then answer these questions.

18. This reaction has one *reactant*. Name that reactant. _____

19. The reactant in its *natural* state is a _____.
    <small>solid, liquid, gas</small>

20. The reactant _____ dangerous.
    <small>is, is not</small>

21. Name the *products*. _____ _____

22. What is the state of sodium? _____

23. **a)** Is sodium dangerous? _____

    b) Are the properties of sodium the same as the properties of sodium chloride?

    _____

24. What is the state of chlorine? _____

25. **a)** Is chlorine dangerous? _____

    b) Are the properties of chlorine the same as the properties of sodium chloride?

    _____

26. In a chemical reaction, properties _____ change.
    <small>do, do not</small>

27. Name the *kinds* of atoms on the reactant side of this equation. _____

28. Name the *kinds* of atoms on the product side. _____ _____

29. **a)** The kinds of atoms on the reactant side _____ the same as the atoms on the resultant side.
    <small>are, are not</small>

    b) Are they in the same form? _____

    c) How are they different? Reactant side _____

    Product side _____

75

30. The arrangement of the atoms _____ changed.
                                        has, has not

31. In this reaction, atoms have _____.
                                      separated, linked up

32. In a chemical reaction, the arrangement of the elements _____
change.   does, does not

COMPLETING SENTENCES   Complete the sentences with the choices below.

---

products	right	physical
chemical equation	take part	yields
new	chemical	reaction
arrow	reactants	left

1. A change in which *no* new products are formed is called a _____ change.

2. A change in which new products *are* formed is called a _____ change.

3. Another way of saying "chemical change" is "chemical _____."

4. A set of symbols and formulas that describes a chemical reaction is called a

_____.

5. A chemical equation tells which substances _____ in a chemical

reaction. It also tells which _____ substances are formed.

6. The substances that take part in a chemical reaction are called the

_____.

7. The new substances that form in a chemical reaction are called the

_____.

8. In a chemical equation, the reactants are on the _____ side. The

products are on the _____ side.

9. In a chemical reaction, the reactants and products are separated by an

_____.

10. The arrow means "produces" or "_____".

NAME _____

76

MATCHING   Match the two lists. Write the correct letter on the line next to each number.

1. _____ chemical reaction

2. _____ chemical equation

3. _____ reactants

4. _____ products

5. _____ physical change

a) substances that are changed in a chemical reaction

b) does not produce new products

c) produces new products

d) new substances from a chemical reaction

e) describes a chemical reaction

IDENTIFYING THE PARTS OF AN EQUATION

Look at the equation in the box. In each of the blanks below the equation, write *reactant*, *product*, or *yield*.

$$NaCl + AgNO_3 \longrightarrow NaNO_3 + AgCl$$

_____ _____ _____

Now look at the list below. There you will find the *name* of each substance in this equation.

Write *reactant* next to each substance that is a reactant.

Write *product* next to each substance that is a product.

Sodium nitrate _____   Sodium chloride _____

Silver nitrate _____   Silver chloride _____

Now do the same for each of the equations that follow.

1. $$Zn + FeSO_4 \longrightarrow ZnSO_4 + Fe$$

Zinc sulfate _____

Zinc _____

Iron _____

Iron sulfate _____

2.

$$4HCl + MnO_2 \longrightarrow MnCl_2 + 2H_2O + Cl_2$$

Chlorine _____

Manganese chloride _____

Manganese dioxide _____

Water _____

Hydrochloric acid (Hydrogen chloride) _____

3.

$$H_2SO_4 + BaCl_2 \longrightarrow 2HCl + BaSO_4$$

Barium chloride _____

Barium sulfate _____

Hydrochloric acid (hydrogen chloride) _____

Sulfuric acid (hydrogen sulfate) _____

4.

$$Br_2 + 2KI \longrightarrow 2KBr + I_2$$

Potassium bromide _____   Iodine _____

Bromine _____   Potassium iodide _____

5.

$$2ZnS + 3O_2 \longrightarrow 2ZnO + 2SO_2$$

Oxygen _____   Sulfur dioxide _____

Zinc oxide _____   Zinc sulfide _____

REACHING OUT

Sodium hydroxide reacts with hydrochloric acid (hydrogen chloride) to produce sodium chloride (table salt) and water. Write the equation that shows this reaction.

_____

NAME _____

DOES A CHEMICAL REACTION DESTROY MATTER?

13

Reactants   Products

Law of Conservation of Matter: the scientific statement that says that a chemical reaction does not destroy or create matter

AIM 13 | Does a chemical reaction destroy matter?

In a chemical reaction, atoms change the way they are linked together. New products form. But are any atoms *lost* during the changeover? Is any matter destroyed?

The *burning of wood* and *rusting* are two examples of chemical reactions.

- Wood burns, and a small amount of ash remains behind.

- A car rusts, and it looks like it's wearing away.

It surely *seems* that some matter is lost. But is it really? This is how we can find out:

1. Weigh the *reactants*. That means weigh *all* the substances that take part in a chemical reaction.

2. Then weigh the *products*. That means weigh *all* the new substances that form.

If there is a *loss* of weight, then we know that some matter was destroyed.

If there is *no* loss of weight, then we know that matter was not destroyed.

In any chemical reaction, there is *no weight loss*. The weight of the products is the same as the weight of the reactants. In other words, we end up with the same weight as we started with. This means that no matter was destroyed.

In a chemical reaction, matter is not destroyed. This is part of a scientific statement called the *Law of Conservation of Matter*.

Can matter be destroyed? Yes! But not in a chemical reaction. It takes an atomic or *nuclear* reaction to destroy matter. When matter is destroyed, it changes into energy. This is the idea behind atomic energy.

NAME _____

UNDERSTANDING THE LAW OF CONSERVATION OF MATTER

Look at Figures A and B. Then answer the questions.

THE BURNING OF WOOD

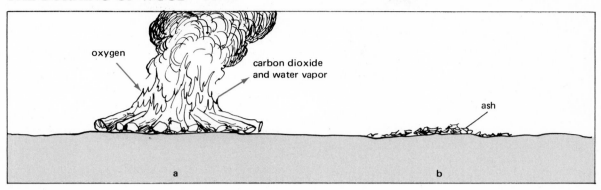

Figure A

Wood, like paper, is made up mostly of carbon and hydrogen.

When wood burns, it links up with oxygen. The reaction produces *ash, carbon dioxide,* and *water vapor.* (Heat energy is also produced. But energy has no weight.)

Wood + Oxygen   →   Ash + Carbon dioxide + Water vapor

1. **a)** Name the *reactants* when wood burns. _____

   b) Name the *products.* _____

2. Where does the oxygen come from? _____

3. The ash remains behind. What happens to the carbon dioxide and water?

   _____

4. If the reactants weigh 10 kilograms, how much will the products weigh?

   _____

5. Is any matter lost? _____

6. Is matter lost during *any* chemical reaction? _____

7. In a chemical reaction, the weight of the products equals the weight of the

   _____. In other words, "the weight you start with is the weight

   _____."

8. Name the scientific statement that tells us that *matter is not destroyed during a*

   chemical reaction. _____

   _____

THE RUSTING OF IRON

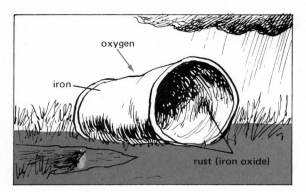

Figure B

When iron rusts, it links up with oxygen. This is the formula for the reaction:

$$4Fe + 3O_2 \longrightarrow 2Fe_2O_3$$

Iron   Oxygen   Iron oxide*
                                     (Rust)

9. Name the *reactants.* _____

_____

10. Where did the oxygen come from? _____

11. There is one *product.* **a)** What is its *chemical* name? _____

     b) What is its *common* name? _____

Look at the equation.

REACTANTS

12. **a)** How many atoms of *iron* did we start with? _____

     b) What is the weight of *all* the *iron* atoms?

        (The atomic weight of iron is 56.) _____

13. **a)** How many atoms of *oxygen* did we start with? _____

     b) What is the weight of *all* the oxygen atoms? _____

        (The atomic weight of oxygen is 16.)

14. Altogether, what is the weight of the *reactants?* _____
                                           total weight of reactants

PRODUCT

15. **a)** How many atoms of iron did we *end* with? _____

     b) What is the weight of all these atoms? _____

16. **a)** How many atoms of oxygen did we *end* with? _____

     b) What is the weight of all these atoms? _____

17. Altogether, what is the weight of the product? _____
                                         total weight of product

---

*Iron oxide is the same as Ferric oxide.

NAME _____

82

18. Is the weight of the product the same as the weight of the reactants? _____

19. a) Was any matter lost? _____

    b) How do you know? _____

_____

20. Is any matter destroyed in a chemical reaction? _____

21. What happens to atoms during a chemical reaction? _____

_____

22. The equation for rusting is a "balanced" equation. What do you think this means?

_____

_____

       Let's work with the equation in a different way. This time let's *just count* atoms.

$$4Fe + 3O_2 \longrightarrow 2Fe_2O_3$$

23. Name the *kinds* of atoms of the *reactant* side of the equation. _____

_____

24. Name the *kinds* of atoms on the *product* side. _____ _____

25. The kinds of atoms on the *product* side _____ the same as the kinds
$$\text{are, are not}$$
of atoms on the reactant side.

26. How many atoms of iron are there on the *reactant* side? _____

27. How many atoms of iron are there on the *product* side? _____

28. How many atoms of oxygen are there on the *reactant* side? _____

29. How many atoms of oxygen are there on the *product* side? _____

30. a) The *number* of each kind of atom _____ the same on both sides
                                           is, is not
      of the equation.

    b) If the number of each kind of atom is the same on both sides of the equation,

       then what else is equal? _____

    c) This shows that matter _____ destroyed.
                        was, was not

PROVING THAT MATTER IS NOT DESTROYED DURING A CHEMICAL REACTION

Figure C

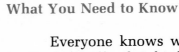

What You Need to Know

Everyone knows what a flashbulb is. It gives off a bright flash of light. It lets us take pictures where there is little light.

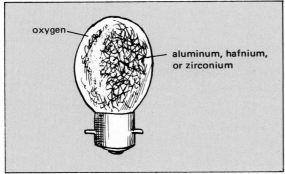

Figure D
Fresh flashbulb

A flashbulb contains oxygen and shreds of metal like aluminum, hafnium, or zirconium.

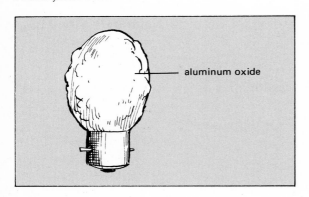

Figure E
Used flashbulb

When a bulb "goes off," a chemical reaction takes place. The oxygen links up with the metal. This produces an *oxide* of the metal. For example, if the bulb contains aluminum, *aluminum oxide* forms.

This is the equation for the reaction:

$$4Al + 3O_2 \longrightarrow 2Al_2O_3 \text{ (+ Light + Heat energy)}$$
Aluminum
oxide

NAME _____

84

What You Need balance scale
6 volt battery
two insulated wires
asbestos pad
fireproof cloth
a flashbulb

What To Do

1. Weigh the bulb *before* you flash it. How much does the bulb weigh?

   _____ grams

2. Place the bulb on the asbestos pad. Cover most of the bulb with the fireproof cloth. Keep only the end of the metal base uncovered. (Figure G)

3. Flash the bulb. (Figure H)

4. Uncover the bulb. Wait about one minute until it cools. Then weigh it again. (Figure I)

   How much does the bulb weigh

   now? _____ grams

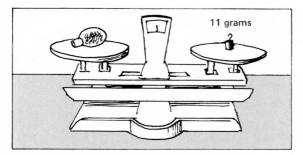

Figure F

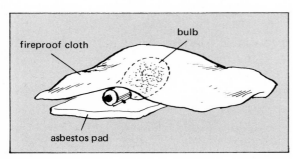

Figure G

What You Learned

5. How much did the bulb weigh *before* it was flashed? _____

6. How much did the bulb weigh *after* it was flashed? _____

7. A flashbulb "going off" causes a

   _____ change.
   physical, chemical

8. If a chemical reaction destroys matter, then the bulb would become

   _____ .
   heavier, lighter

9. Did the bulb become lighter after it was flashed? _____

10. Matter _____ destroyed.
    was, was not

11. A chemical reaction _____ destroy matter.
    does, does not

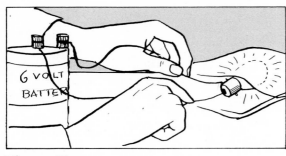

Figure H

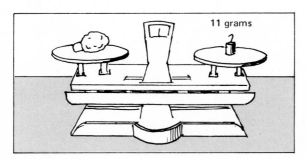

Figure I

BALANCED OR NOT BALANCED?

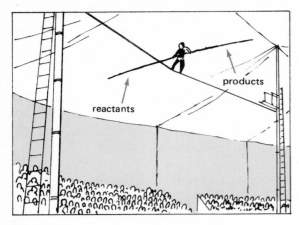

Figure J

Four equations are listed below. Two are balanced. Two are not. Figure out which ones are balanced. (Hint: Counting atoms is the easiest way.)

Equation

I $Zn + H_2SO_4 \longrightarrow ZnSO_4 + H_2$

II $Mg + O_2 \longrightarrow 2MgO$

III $Na_2S + 2HCl \longrightarrow 2NaCl + H_2S$

IV $H_2S + SO_2 \longrightarrow 3S + 2H_2O$

1. Which equations *are* balanced? _____

2. Which equations are *not* balanced? _____

3. Which equations show the Law of Conservation of Matter? _____

4. Which equations do *not* show the Law of Conservation of Matter? _____

_____

5. Which equations are not possible? _____

Figure K *Uranium fuel*

REACHING OUT

A nuclear reaction *destroys* matter. Nuclear fuel, like uranium, changes to *energy*.

However, *no* kind of reaction—nuclear or chemical—is known to *create* matter.

How can we show that a chemical reaction does not *create* matter? (Hint: Look back at the flashbulb experiment.) _____

_____

NAME _____

WHAT IS A SYNTHESIS REACTION?

14

synthesis: the combining of several substances to form a more complicated substance

AIM 14 | What is a synthesis reaction?

Chemical reactions are happening around you all the time. A match burns. A car rusts. Food spoils. Leaves decay. These are just a few chemical reactions.

Probably the most important chemical reactions take place in your body. They are happening this very moment. *Digestion* is a chemical process. So is *respiration*. In every one of your *trillions* of cells, chemical reactions are taking place all the time. Life *depends* upon chemical reactions.

There are several kinds of chemical reactions. One kind is the *synthesis* [SIN thuh sis] reaction. "Synthesis" means *a putting together*. A synthesis reaction *combines* substances, *usually* elements, to form a compound. When the compound forms, we say it has been *synthesized*. Below is a "model" of a synthesis reaction.

$$A \; + \; B \; \longrightarrow \; AB$$
Element + Element $\longrightarrow$ Compound

Let's study two synthesis reactions.

1. RUSTING   When iron rusts, it *combines* with oxygen.

    Remember this equation?

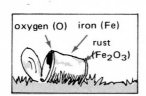

$$4Fe \; + \; 3O_2 \; \longrightarrow \; 2Fe_2O_3$$
Iron + Oxygen $\longrightarrow$ Iron oxide (rust)

Element + Element $\xrightarrow[\text{to form}]{\text{link up}}$ Compound

2. THE BURNING OF CARBON   Charcoal is made of the element carbon (C). When carbon burns, it *combines* with oxygen. This produces the gas carbon dioxide (CO_2).

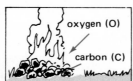

$$C \; + \; O_2 \; \longrightarrow \; CO_2$$
Carbon + Oxygen $\xrightarrow[\text{to form}]{\text{link up}}$ Carbon dioxide

Element + Element $\longrightarrow$ Compound

A synthesis reaction is like *any* other kind of chemical reaction. No matter is created. No matter is destroyed. The atoms just change their arrangement.

NAME _____

UNDERSTANDING SYNTHESIS REACTIONS

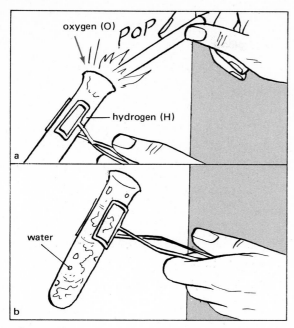

Figure A

Look at Figures A, B, and C, and read the explanation. Then answer the questions with each.

When hydrogen explodes, it combines with oxygen.

Water is produced.

The equation shows what happens:

$$H_2 \ + \ O_2 \longrightarrow H_2O$$
Hydrogen + Oxygen $\longrightarrow$ Water

1. Hydrogen is _____.
   an element, a compound

2. Oxygen is _____.
   an element, a compound

3. Water is _____.
   an element, a compound

4. Is the formation of water a synthesis reaction? _____

5. Why is the formation of water a synthesis reaction? _____

6. A compound has at least one metal and one nonmetal. In the synthesis of water, which is the metal, hydrogen or oxygen? (Hint: Look at the formula for water.)

_____

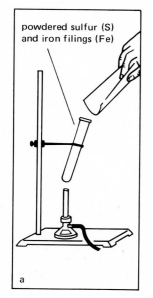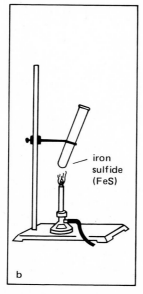

Figure B

When powdered sulfur and iron filings are heated together, they form *iron sulfide.*

This equation shows what happens:

$$Fe \ + \ S \longrightarrow FeS$$
Iron + Sulfur $\longrightarrow$ Iron sulfide

7. Iron is _____.
   an element, a compound

8. Sulfur is _____.
   an element, a compound

9. Iron sulfide is _____.
   an element, a compound

89

10. What happens to the iron and sulfur when they form iron sulfide? _____

_____

11. Why is the formation of iron sulfide a synthesis reaction? _____

_____

12. In the synthesis of iron sulfide, which element is the metal? _____

Figure C

Sodium combines with chlorine to form sodium chloride—common table salt.

This equation shows what happens:

$$Na + Cl \longrightarrow NaCl$$

Sodium + Chlorine $\longrightarrow$ Sodium chloride

13. Sodium is _____.
          an element, a compound

14. Chlorine is _____.
          an element, a compound

15. Sodium chloride is _____.
          an element, a compound

16. a) What kind of reaction is the formation of sodium chloride? _____

    b) Why? _____

17. In the synthesis of sodium chloride, which element is the *nonmetal*? _____

YOUR OWN WORDS, PLEASE

1. What does "synthesis" mean? _____

_____

2. What does "synthesis reaction" mean? _____

_____

Two synthesis equations are shown on the next page. They are different from the ones you have read about in this Aim.

NAME _____

Equation I $CO_2 + C \longrightarrow 2CO_2$

Equation II $CO_2 + H_2O \longrightarrow H_2CO_3$

3. How is Equation I different from the other synthesis equations in this Aim?

_____

4. How is Equation II different from the other synthesis equations in this Aim?

_____

IDENTIFYING SYNTHESIS REACTIONS

Ten equations are listed below. Some are synthesis reactions. Some are not. Make a check (✓) in the correct box next to each equation.

Equation	A Synthesis Reaction	Not a Synthesis Reaction
1. $2K + Br_2 \longrightarrow 2KBr$		
2. $2H_2O \longrightarrow 2H_2 + O_2$		
3. $NaCl \longrightarrow Na + Cl$		
4. $4Au + 3O_2 \longrightarrow 2Au_2O_3$		
5. $2Na + 2HCl \longrightarrow 2NaCl + H_2$		
6. $Cu + Br_2 \longrightarrow CuBr_2$		
7. $Zn + S \longrightarrow ZnS$		
8. $2Na + Br_2 \longrightarrow 2NaBr$		
9. $2HgO \longrightarrow 2Hg + O_2$		
10. $2Na + I_2 \longrightarrow 2NaI$		

TRUE OR FALSE Write T on the line next to the number if the sentence is true. Write F if the sentence is false.

_____

1. _____ There is only one kind of chemical reaction.

2. _____ A synthesis reaction separates a compound into its elements.

3. _____ The *reactants* of *every* synthesis reaction are elements.

4. _____ The *product* of a synthesis reaction is a compound.

5. _____ Chemical reactions take place only in the laboratory.

REACHING OUT

Most compounds made of only two elements have names ending in *-ide*. For example:

$$NaCl = \text{sodium } chloride$$
$$K_2S = \text{potassium } sulfide$$

Can you name these compounds?

	Formula	Name
1.	CaO	
2.	KI	
3.	NaBr	
4.	AgF	
5.	MgCl	

WORD SEARCH The words in this list are hidden within the groups of letters. Try to find each word. When you find it, draw a line around the word. The spelling may go in any direction.

MATTER
POLYVALENT
RADICAL
WEIGHT
REACTANT
FORMULA
PHYSICAL
PRODUCT
YIELDS
CHEMICAL

C	T	L	A	C	I	S	Y	H	P	A
H	O	N	L	A	C	I	M	E	H	C
I	Y	I	E	L	D	S	C	N	O	D
M	I	C	A	L	U	M	R	O	F	M
T	N	A	T	C	A	E	R	T	T	Y
N	E	L	E	H	W	V	H	G	C	L
R	I	A	L	D	E	A	Y	L	U	L
A	L	R	A	D	I	C	A	L	D	I
I	S	Y	R	A	G	L	E	Y	O	M
J	E	R	R	Y	H	D	W	I	R	P
C	L	R	E	T	T	A	M	E	P	I

NAME _____

WHAT IS A DECOMPOSITION REACTION?

15

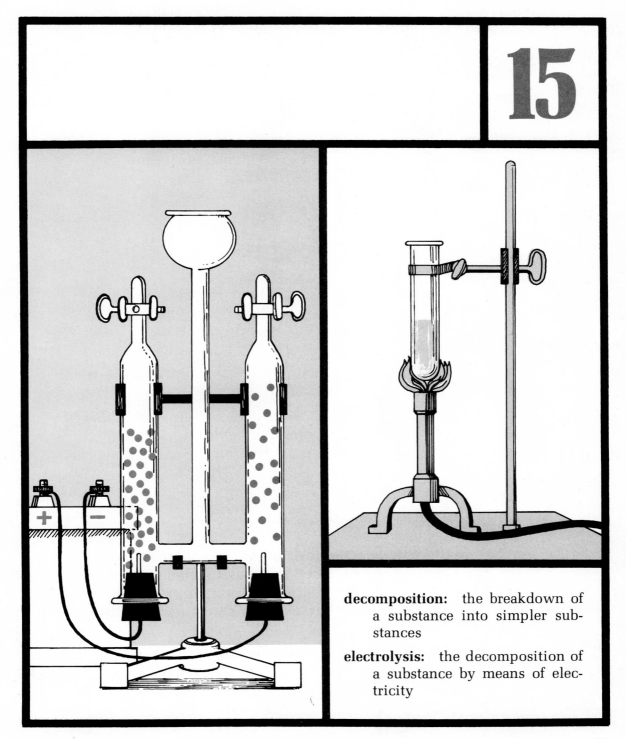

decomposition: the breakdown of a substance into simpler substances

electrolysis: the decomposition of a substance by means of electricity

AIM 15 | What is a decomposition reaction?

Synthesis reactions *build* compounds. Anything that can be built can also be taken apart. The breakdown of a compound into simpler substances is called *decomposition* [DEE com puh ZISH un]. Decomposition is a *chemical* process.

Let's look at two examples.

1. Common table salt (sodium chloride) is a compound. It is composed of the elements *sodium* and *chlorine.*

Sodium chloride can be melted. If electricity is passed through melted sodium chloride, it *decomposes.* The molecules unlock. They change back to atoms of sodium and chlorine. This equation shows the reaction:

$$2\,NaCl \xrightarrow[\text{into}]{\text{breaks down}} 2\,Na \ + \ Cl_2$$

Sodium chloride   Sodium   Chlorine
(compound)   (element)   (element)

The decomposition of a compound by means of electricity is called *electrolysis* [i lek TROL i sis]. Only certain compounds can be decomposed by electrolysis. Usually these compounds are liquids.

2. Potassium chlorate ($KClO_3$) is a compound. It is composed of the elements *potassium, chlorine,* and *oxygen.*

Heat decomposes potassium chlorate. Potassium chlorate changes to oxygen and potassium chloride (a simpler compound). This equation shows the reaction:

$$2\,KClO_3 \longrightarrow 2\,KCl \ + \ 3\,O_2$$

Potassium   Potassium   Oxygen
chlorate   chloride   (element)
(compound)   (a simpler
                      compound)

Notice that the decomposition is not complete. The oxygen has been separated. But the potassium and chlorine are still joined to form the compound potassium chloride. Another kind of decomposition reaction can separate potassium chloride into its elements.

Only certain compounds are decomposed with heat.

NAME _____

UNDERSTANDING DECOMPOSITION REACTIONS

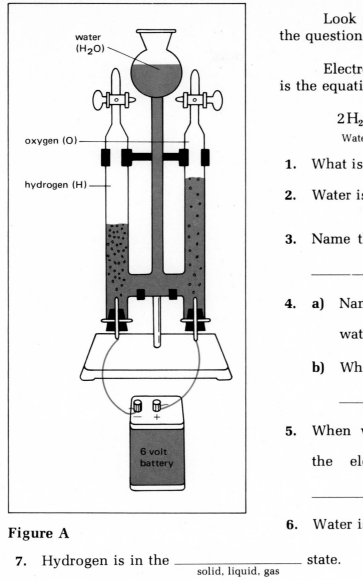

water
(H₂O)

oxygen (O)

hydrogen (H)

6 volt
battery

Figure A

Look at Figures A and B. Then answer the questions or fill in the blanks.

Electrolysis decomposes water. This is the equation for the reaction:

$$2H_2O \quad \rightarrow \quad 2H_2 \quad + \quad O_2$$

Water   Hydrogen + Oxygen

1. What is the formula for water? _____

2. Water is _____.
   <u>an element, a compound</u>

3. Name the elements that make up water.

   _____ _____

4. **a)** Name the *process* that decomposes

   water. _____

   b) What kind of *energy* is used?

   _____

5. When water decomposes, it changes to

   the elements _____ and

   _____.

6. Water is in the _____ state.
   <u>solid, liquid, gas</u>

7. Hydrogen is in the _____ state.
   <u>solid, liquid, gas</u>

8. Oxygen is in the _____ state.
   <u>solid, liquid, gas</u>

9. Which is simpler, water or the atoms that make up water? _____

10. Decomposition _____ compounds.
    <u>builds up, breaks down</u>

11. Can electrolysis decompose every compound? _____

12. Name another compound that can be decomposed with electrolysis.

    _____

13. A compound that can be separated by electrolysis must be in which state of matter?

    _____

Look at Figure B.

Mercuric oxide is a solid. Heat decomposes mercuric oxide. This is the equation for the reaction:

$$2\,\text{HgO} \xrightarrow{\text{heat}} 2\,\text{Hg} + \text{O}_2$$

Mercuric   Mercury + Oxygen
oxide

14. What is the formula for mercuric oxide? _____

15. Mercuric oxide is _____ .
                        an element, a compound

16. Name the elements that make up mercuric oxide. _____

_____

17. What kind of energy decomposes mercuric oxide? _____

18. When mercuric oxide decomposes, it changes to the elements _____

and _____ .

19. Mercuric oxide is in the _____ state.
                               solid, liquid, gas

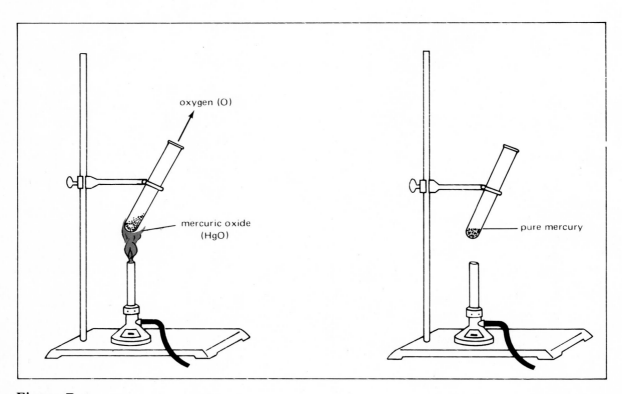

Figure B

NAME _____

96

20. Mercury is in the _____ state.
solid, liquid, gas

21. Oxygen is in the _____ state.
solid, liquid, gas

22. Which is simpler: mercuric oxide or the elements that make up mercuric oxide?

_____

23. The mercury _____.
stays in the test tube, escapes into the air

24. The oxygen _____.
stays in the test tube, escapes into the air

25. Can heat decompose every compound? _____

26. Name another compound that can be decomposed by heat. _____

COMPLETING SENTENCES   Complete the sentences with the choices below.

heating	mercuric oxide	electrolysis
potassium chlorate	synthesis	molten sodium chloride
liquid	fewer	decomposition
simpler	water	

1. The *combining* of substances to form a compound is called _____.

2. The *breakdown* of a compound into simpler substances is called _____.

3. Two methods used to decompose compounds are _____ and

_____.

4. For a compound to decompose by electrolysis, it must be in a _____ state.

5. Two compounds that can be decomposed by electrolysis are _____

and _____.

6. Two compounds that can be decomposed by heat are _____ and

_____.

7. Atoms are _____ than molecules.

8. KCl is a simpler compound than $KClO_3$ because KCl has _____ elements and atoms.

MATCHING Match the two lists. Write the correct letter on the line next to each number.

1. _____ synthesis reaction
2. _____ decomposition reaction
3. _____ electrolysis and heat
4. _____ electrolysis
5. _____ an element

a) breaks down compounds
b) uses electricity
c) methods of decomposition
d) simpler than a compound
e) builds compounds

IDENTIFYING DECOMPOSITION REACTIONS

Ten chemical equations are listed below. Some are decomposition reactions. Some are not. Mark a check (√) in the correct box next to each equation.

	Equation	Decomposition Reaction	Not a Decomposition Reaction
1.	$CuCl_2 \longrightarrow Cu + Cl_2$		
2.	$3Hf + 2N_2 \longrightarrow Hf_3N_4$		
3.	$Zn + 2HCl \longrightarrow ZnCl_2 + H_2$		
4.	$H_2CO_3 \longrightarrow H_2O + CO_2$		
5.	$2NaOH \longrightarrow 2Na + O_2 + H_2$		
6.	$Fe + S \longrightarrow FeS$		
7.	$CaCO_3 \longrightarrow CaO + CO_2$		
8.	$4P + 5O_2 \longrightarrow 2P_2O_5$		
9.	$C + O_2 \longrightarrow CO_2$		
10.	$Ca(OH)_2 \longrightarrow CaO + H_2O$		

REACHING OUT

1. Does boiling decompose water? _____

2. What does boiling do to water? _____

NAME _____

WHAT IS A REPLACEMENT REACTION?

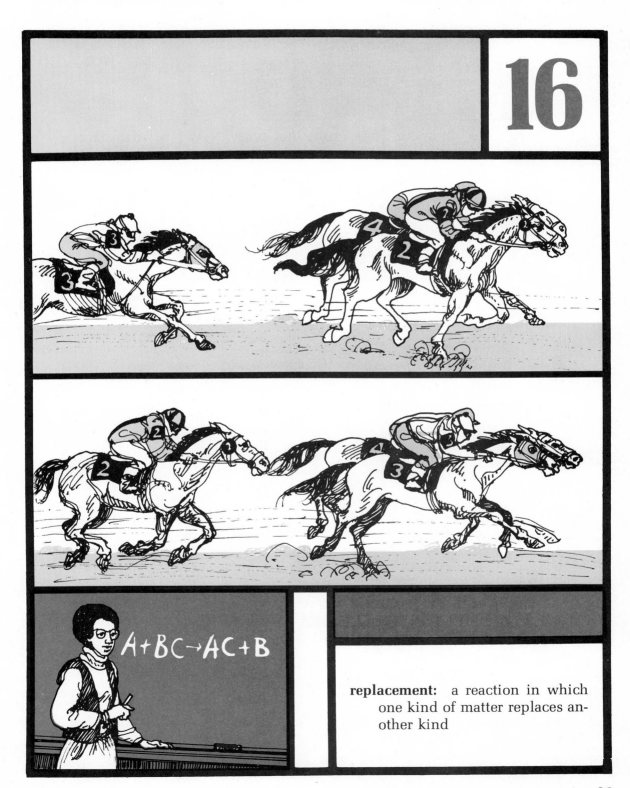

16

A + BC → AC + B

replacement: a reaction in which one kind of matter replaces another kind

AIM 16 | What is a replacement reaction?

Imagine that three children are playing.

Two are holding hands. The other is alone.

The child that was alone now joins the others. He takes the place of one of the children.

Now a different child is alone.

We have the same children that we started with. But, now they are arranged in a different way.

Some chemical reactions work like this. A free element takes the place of or replaces another element of a compound.

The element that was replaced is now "free."

$$\underset{\text{free element}}{A} + \underset{\text{compound}}{BC} \longrightarrow \underset{\text{new compound}}{AC} + \underset{\text{new free element}}{B}$$

Let's study an actual replacement reaction—one between zinc (Zn) and hydrochloric acid (HCl).

The zinc is the "free" element. The hydrochloric acid is in the compound.

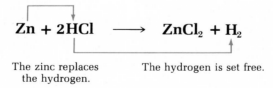

$$Zn + 2HCl \longrightarrow ZnCl_2 + H_2$$

The zinc replaces the hydrogen.

The hydrogen is set free.

The reaction produces a new compound, zinc chloride ($ZnCl_2$), and free hydrogen (H_2). Notice that the elements we started with are the elements we ended with. They are just arranged in a different way.

This kind of reaction is called a *single replacement reaction*. In a single replacement reaction, a free element replaces a different element of a compound.

NAME _____

UNDERSTANDING SINGLE REPLACEMENT REACTIONS

Figure A

What You Need
iron nail
copper sulfate solution
beaker

How To Do The Experiment

Place an iron nail in copper sulfate solution.

Remove the nail in a few minutes.

What You Saw

The nail is coated with copper.

This is the equation for the reaction.

$$Fe + CuSO_4 \longrightarrow FeSO_4 + Cu$$

Iron   Copper sulfate   Iron sulfate   Copper

Answer these questions.

1. Name the *free element* we started with. _____

2. Name the *compound* we started with. _____

3. Name the *free element* we ended with. _____

4. Name the *compound* we ended with. _____

5. **a)** Which element did the iron replace? _____

   b) What happened to this element? _____

6. What do we call this kind of chemical reaction? _____

7. What happens during a single replacement reaction? _____

IDENTIFYING SINGLE REPLACEMENT REACTIONS

Six equations are listed below. Some are single replacement reactions. Some are not. Mark a check (√) in the correct box next to each equation.

	Equation	Single replacement reaction	Not a single replacement reaction
1.	$C + 2S \longrightarrow CS_2$		
2.	$H_2O_2 \longrightarrow H_2 + O_2$		
3.	$2Al + 6HCl \longrightarrow 2AlCl_3 + 3H_2$		
4.	$2K + Cl_2 \longrightarrow 2KCl$		
5.	$Zn + PbO \longrightarrow ZnO + Pb$		
6.	$Fe + CuSO_4 \longrightarrow FeSO_4 + Cu$		

DOUBLE REPLACEMENT REACTIONS

A *single* replacement reaction takes place between an element and a compound. The free element replaces one of the elements of the compound. This produces a new compound and a new free element.

$$A + BC \longrightarrow AC + B$$

free element   compound   new compound   new free element

A *double* replacement reaction takes place between two *compounds*. A part of one compound changes place with a part of the other compound.

Let's use playing children as models again to see what happens.

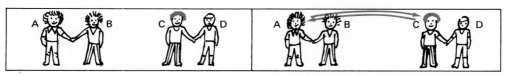

Children A and B stand for compound AB.

Children C and D stand for compound CD.

Child A changes place with child C.

What do we have now? Instead of compound AB + CD, we have two *new* compounds—CB and AD.

When there are two changeovers, *a double* replacement has taken place.

NAME _____

Now let's study an *actual* double replacement reaction—the reaction between sodium hydroxide (NaOH), and hydrochloric acid (HCl).

$$NaOH + HCl \longrightarrow NaCl + HOH*$$

- The sodium and hydrogen change places.

- Two new *compounds* form—NaCl (common table salt) and HOH (water).

Now you try. Read each equation carefully. Then answer the questions or fill in the blanks with each.

Equation I. $BaCl_2 + Na_2SO_4 \longrightarrow BaSO_4 + 2NaCl$

                 Barium   Sodium   Barium   Sodium
                 chloride   sulfate   sulfate   chloride

1. Name the reactants.   _____   _____

2. The reactants are   _____ .
                       all elements, all compounds, an element and a compound

3. The barium changed places with the _____ .
                                     sulfate, chlorine, sodium

4. Name the products.   _____   _____

5. The products are _____ .
                     all elements, all compounds, an element and a compound

6. What kind of chemical reaction is this?   _____

7. Double replacement is the reaction of two _____ to form two new

      _____ .

Equation II. $AgNO_3 + NaBr \longrightarrow AgBr + NaNO_3$

                   Silver   Sodium   Silver   Sodium
                   nitrate   bromide   bromide   nitrate

8. Name the reactants.   _____   _____

9. The reactants are   _____ .
                       all elements, all compounds, an element and a compound

10. The silver changed places with the _____ .
                                  sodium, bromine, nitrate

11. Name the products.   _____   _____

12. The products are _____ .
                     all elements, all compounds, an element and a compound

13. What kind of chemical reaction is this?   _____

_____

*The formula for water may be written HOH as well as H_2O.

IDENTIFYING DOUBLE REPLACEMENT REACTIONS

Eight equations are listed below. Some are double replacement reactions. Some are not. Mark a check (√) in the correct box next to each equation.

	Equation	Double replacement reaction	Not a double replacement reaction
1.	$Mg(OH_2) + 2HCl \longrightarrow MgCl_2 + 2HOH$		
2.	$C_6H_{10}O_5 + H_2O \longrightarrow C_6H_{12}O_6$		
3.	$Na_2SO_4 + BaCl_2 \longrightarrow 2NaCl + BaSO_4$		
4.	$3Mg + N_2 \longrightarrow Mg_3N_2$		
5.	$H_2SO_4 + BaCl_2 \longrightarrow 2HCl + BaSO_4$		
6.	$ZnCO_3 \longrightarrow ZnO + CO_2$		
7.	$CuSO_4 + H_2S \longrightarrow H_2SO_4 + CuS$		
8.	$NH_4NO_3 \longrightarrow 2H_2O + N_2O$		

IDENTIFYING CHEMICAL REACTIONS

Ten chemical equations are listed below. Identify each kind of reaction: *synthesis, decomposition, single replacement,* or *double replacement.*

Equation	Kind of reaction
1. $N_2 + 3H_2 \longrightarrow 2NH_3$	
2. $2Br_2 + 2H_2O \longrightarrow 4HBr + O_2$	
3. $Mg + 2HCl \longrightarrow MgCl_2 + H_2$	
4. $2KBr + H_2SO_4 \longrightarrow K_2SO_4 + 2HBr$	
5. $H_2SO_3 \longrightarrow H_2O + SO_2$	
6. $Na_2S + 2HCl \longrightarrow 2NaCl + H_2S$	
7. $2Na + I_2 \longrightarrow 2NaI$	
8. $NaCl + AgNO_3 \longrightarrow NaNO_3 + AgCl$	
9. $H_2 + Cl_2 \longrightarrow 2HCl$	
10. $H_2CO_3 \longrightarrow H_2O + CO_2$	

NAME _____

WHAT ARE OXIDATION AND REDUCTION?

17

TESTED 500 LBS. CO_2

FIRE EXTINGUISHER

CAUTION: PRESSURE VESSEL

oxidation: the linkup of oxygen with another substance; a loss of electrons

reduction: the separation of oxygen from a substance; a gain of electrons

AIM 17 | What are oxidation and reduction?

Oxidation and reduction are opposite kinds of chemical reactions.

> *Oxidation* takes place when oxygen *combines* with another substance.

For example, when a flashbulb goes off, oxygen *combines* with aluminum.

The aluminum becomes *oxidized*. Aluminum oxide (Al_2O_3) forms.

$$4\,Al \ + \ 3\,O_2 \ \longrightarrow \ 2\,Al_2O_3$$

Aluminum   Oxygen   Aluminum oxide

> *Reduction* takes place when oxygen *separates* from a compound.

For example, electrolysis decomposes molten aluminum oxide (Al_2O_3). The oxygen *separates* from the aluminum. We say the aluminum oxide is *reduced*.

$$2\,Al_2O_3 \ \longrightarrow \ 4\,Al \ + \ 3\,O_2$$

Aluminum oxide   Aluminum   Oxygen

Here is another reduction equation. Notice what happens to the oxygen.

$$2\,Fe_2O_3 + \ 3\,C \ \longrightarrow \ 3\,CO_2 + 4\,Fe$$

Iron   Carbon   Carbon   Iron
oxide   dioxide

The oxygen has separated from the iron. But the oxygen is not *free* oxygen. It is now part of the *compound* carbon dioxide. It makes no difference whether the separated oxygen becomes free oxygen or part of a new compound. As long as oxygen is separated from a compound, the reaction is *reduction*.

NAME _____

UNDERSTANDING OXIDATION AND REDUCTION

Look at Figures A and B. Study the equations. Then answer the questions or fill in the blanks with each.

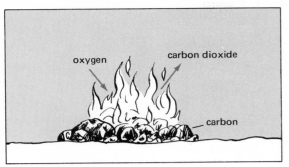

Figure A

The burning of carbon

The equation describes what happens when carbon burns:

$$C + O_2 \longrightarrow CO_2$$

1. Name the elements that react together when carbon burns.

   _____ _____

2. **a)** When carbon burns, oxygen _____ the carbon.
   combines with, separates from

   b) What product forms? _____

3. In *oxidation*, oxygen _____ another substance.
   combines with, separates from

4. In *reduction*, oxygen

   _____ a
   combines with, separates from
   compound.

5. **a)** When carbon burns, the carbon

   is _____.
   oxidized, reduced

   b) This is because the oxygen

   _____ the
   combines with, separates from
   carbon.

The electrolysis of water

The equation for the electrolysis of water is:

$$2H_2O \longrightarrow 2H_2 + O_2$$

6. Name the elements that make up water. _____

   _____

7. Electrolysis _____ water.
   forms, decomposes

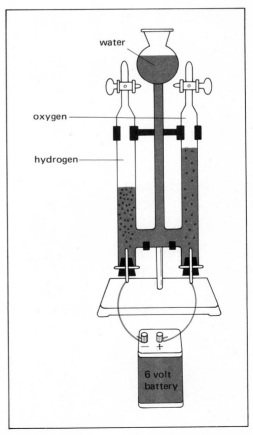

Figure B

8. When water decomposes, oxygen _____ hydrogen.
combines with, separates from

9. The separation of oxygen from a compound is called _____.
oxidation, reduction

10. **a)** In the electrolysis of water, the hydrogen is _____.
oxidized, reduced

b) This is because the oxygen _____ the hydrogen.
combines with, separates from

ANOTHER WAY OF EXPLAINING OXIDATION AND REDUCTION

Oxidation *combines* oxygen with another substance.

Reduction *separates* oxygen from a compound.

This is true. But to a chemist, oxidation and reduction mean even more. A chemist thinks of oxidation and reduction in terms of *electrons gained or electrons lost.*

To a chemist,

Oxidation means a *loss* of electrons.

Reduction means a *gain* of electrons.

The reaction *may or may not* involve oxygen. This means that oxidation and reduction can happen *without* oxygen. All that is needed is a *loss* of electrons by one atom and the *gain* of electrons by some other atom.

Oxidation and reduction *always happen together.* It's easy to understand why. . . . When one atom *loses* electrons, some other atom *gains* them.

Let's look at the burning of carbon and the electrolysis of water again. This time, look in terms of *electrons gained* and *electrons lost.*

Look at Figures C and D. Answer the questions or fill in the blanks with each.

NAME _____

The burning of carbon

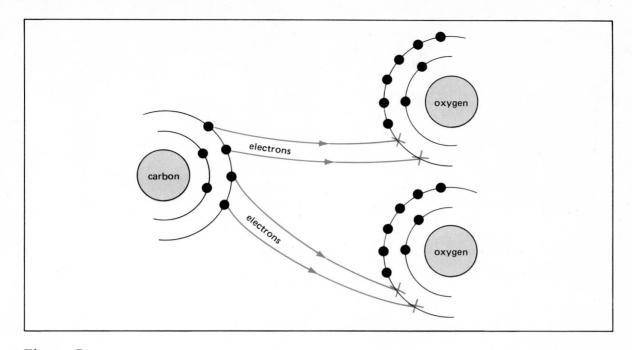

Figure C

Figure C shows what happens when carbon burns.

1. When carbon burns, the carbon _____ electrons and the oxygen
   _{lends, borrows}

   _____ electrons.
   _{lends, borrows}

2. When carbon burns, the carbon _____ electrons and the oxygen
   _{gains, loses}

   _____ electrons.
   _{gains, loses}

3. Oxidation is the _____ of electrons.
   _{gain, loss}

4. Reduction is the _____ of electrons.
   _{gain, loss}

5. When carbon burns, the carbon is _____ and the oxygen is
   _{oxidized, reduced}

   _____ .
   _{oxidized, reduced}

6. Oxidation and reduction happen together because electrons _____

   by one atom are _____ by some other atom.

The electrolysis of water

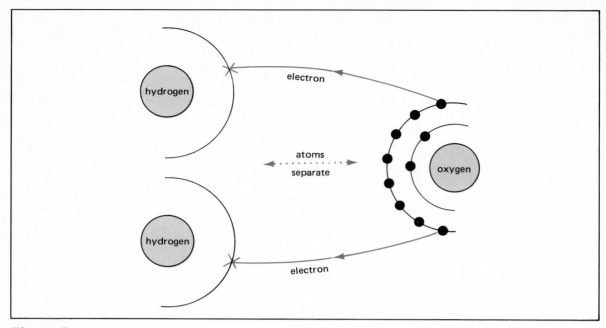

Figure D

Figure D shows what happens during the electrolysis of water.

7. Electrolysis _____ water.
   forms, decomposes

8. When water decomposes, electrons move from the _____ to the
   hydrogen, oxygen

   _____ .
   hydrogen, oxygen

9. The hydrogen _____ electrons and the oxygen _____
   gains, loses   gains, loses

   electrons.

10. Oxidation is the _____ of electrons.
    gain, loss

11. Reduction is the _____ of electrons.
    gain, loss

12. During the electrolysis of water, the hydrogen is _____ and the
    oxidized, reduced

    oxygen is _____ .
    oxidized, reduced

13. Why do oxidation and reduction always happen together? _____

    _____

NAME _____

110

Complete the sentences with the choices below.

gain	loss	linkup
loses	together	oxygen
separation	gains	

1. *Oxidation* has more than one meaning:

    a) Oxidation is the _____ of oxygen with some other substance.

    b) Oxidation is also the _____ of electrons.

2. *Reduction* has more than one meaning:

    a) Reduction is the _____ of oxygen from a compound.

    b) Reduction is also the _____ of electrons.

3. Oxidation does not have to involve _____.

4. Oxidation and reduction happen _____.

5. In a chemical reaction, when one atom _____ electrons, and some other atom _____ them.

SLOW AND RAPID OXIDATION

Figure E

Rusting is an example of slow *oxidation.*

Figure F

Fire is an example of rapid *oxidation.*

Any kind of *burning* is *oxidation*. There is *slow* oxidation and rapid oxidation.

1. Why is *any* kind of burning oxidation? _____

    _____

2. Which kind of oxidation gives off light and heat? _____

OXIDATION OR REDUCTION?

Each equation listed below is either an *oxidation* or a *reduction* reaction. Which one is it? Put a check (√) in the correct box next to each equation.

	Equation	Oxidation	Reduction
1.	$2\,Ba + O_2 \longrightarrow 2\,BaO$		
2.	$2\,HgO \longrightarrow 2\,Hg + O_2$		
3.	$ZnO + C \longrightarrow Zn + CO$		
4.	$4\,Na + O_2 \longrightarrow 2\,Na_2O$		
5.	$CuO + H_2 \longrightarrow Cu + H_2O$		
6.	$N_2 + O_2 \longrightarrow 2\,NO$		
7.	$4\,Ag + O_2 \longrightarrow 2\,Ag_2O$		
8.	$SnO_2 + 2\,C \longrightarrow Sn + 2\,CO$		
9.	$C + O_2 \longrightarrow CO_2$		
10.	$Fe_2O_3 + 3\,CO \longrightarrow 2\,Fe + 3\,CO_2$		

REACHING OUT

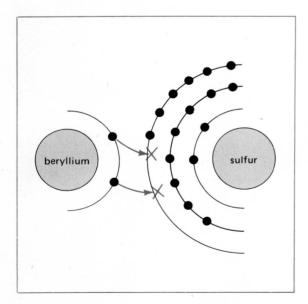

Figure G

Beryllium links up with sulfur to form beryllium sulfide.

$$Be + S \longrightarrow BeS$$

No oxygen is involved in this reaction. Yet it is an oxidation-reduction reaction.

Why is this an oxidation-reduction reaction? _____

_____

NAME _____

WHAT IS AN ORE?

18

mineral: a solid substance found in the earth's crust

ore: a mineral that contains a useful amount of metal

metallurgy: the science of separating metals from the ores in which they are found

metallurgist: a scientist who studies metals

AIM 18 | What is an ore?

Towering skyscrapers, graceful bridges that support millions of kilograms, huge ocean liners, trucks, trains, food cans, even ballpoint pens . . . these are part of our modern world. They all have one thing in common. They could not be possible without metal.

Modern civilization depends upon metals. Yet, we take them for granted. Did you ever wonder where metals come from?

Most metals are found in the earth's *crust*. (We live on the earth's crust.) A few metals, like gold and silver, are found as *free* or *native* minerals. That is, they are not part of any compound. Most minerals, however, are combined chemically with other elements. They are part of mineral *compounds*.

Mineral compounds may be decomposed. This frees the metals so we can use them.

A mineral that can supply a useful metal at reasonable cost is called an *ore*.

There are three main groups of ores: *oxides*, *sulfides*, and *carbonates*.

- Oxides are compounds of *oxygen*. *Hematite* is an example of an oxide ore. Hematite, or iron *oxide* (Fe_2O_3), is the chief iron ore.

- Sulfides are compounds of *sulfur*. Galena is an example of a sulfur ore. Galena, or lead *sulfide* (PbS), is the chief lead ore.

- Carbonates are compounds containing the radical CO_3. *Smithsonite* is an example of a carbonate ore. Smithsonite, or zinc *carbonate* ($ZnCO_3$), is an important zinc ore.

There are several ways to separate ores. The method used depends upon the ore. You will learn how metals are separated from their ores in the next Aim.

The science of separating metals from ores is called *metallurgy* [MET uh lur jee]. A scientist who studies metals is called a *metallurgist*.

NAME _____

UNDERSTANDING ORES

Figure A

Most ores look like ordinary rocks. You would not guess that they contain shiny metal.

The earth's crust is made up of many *minerals*.

1. Most minerals are _____.
elements, compounds

2. In order to free the metal from other elements, a mineral must be

_____.
synthesized, decomposed

Figure B

Figure C

Some ores are mined deep in the ground as in Figure B. However, most ores are mined on the surface. This is called *open-pit* mining. Figure C shows a huge open-pit mine.

3. What is the definition of an ore? _____

_____

4. Many minerals contain metal.

    a) Is every mineral that contains a metal an ore? _____

    b) Why or why not? _____

IDENTIFYING METALS FROM THEIR ORES

The chart below lists some important ores and their formulas.

Which metal do we get from each ore? Look at the formulas. See which metals are shown by their symbols. Write your answers in the column next to the formulas. Then decide if the ore is an oxide, sulfide, or carbonate. Write your answers in the last column.

	Ore	Formula	Metal	Oxide, Sulfide, or Carbonate?
1.	hematite	Fe_2O_3		
2.	galena	PbS		
3.	cinnabar	HgS		
4.	siderite	$FeCO_3$		
5.	bauxite	Al_2O_3		
6.	cassiterite	SnO_2		
7.	magnesite	$MgCO_3$		
8.	smithsonite	$ZnCO_3$		
9.	uraninite	UO_2		
10.	litharge	PbO		
11.	magnetite	Fe_3O_4		
12.	sphalerite	ZnS		
13.	cuprite	Cu_2O		
14.	limonite	Fe_2O_3		
15.	zincite	ZnO		
16.	pyrite	FeS_2		

ELEMENTS OF THE EARTH'S CRUST

The pie graph in Figure D shows the percentage of the most common *elements* that make up the earth's crust.

Study the graph. Then answer the questions.

NAME _____

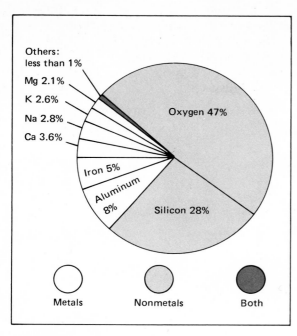

Figure D

1. Most of the earth's crust is made up of _____.
   <small>metals, nonmetals</small>

2. The most common *element* of the earth's crust is _____.

3. The second most common *element* of the earth's crust is _____.

4. a) Together, oxygen and silicon make up _____ percent of the earth's crust.

   b) Write this percent as a fraction.

   _____

5. a) The most common *metal* of the earth's crust is _____.

   b) What percentage of the crust is it? _____

6. a) The second most common *metal* of the earth's crust is _____.

   b) What percentage of the crust is it? _____

7. The six *metals* named in this graph make up about what percent of the earth's crust? _____

MATCHING   Match the two lists. Write the correct letter on the line next to each number.

1. _____ crust

2. _____ carbonate

3. _____ hematite

4. _____ smithsonite

5. _____ galena

a) iron ore

b) lead ore

c) the part of the earth on which we live

d) zinc ore

e) CO_3

COMPLETING SENTENCES

Complete the sentences with the choices below.

crust   sulfides   ore
metallurgist   gold   silver
decomposed   carbonates   oxides
minerals   more   metallurgy

1. Most metals are found in the earth's _____.

2. Metals found *not* combined with other elements are called native elements or native _____.

3. Examples of native minerals are _____ and _____.

4. Most minerals are made up of _____ than one element.

5. To separate a metal from its mineral, the mineral must be _____.

6. A mineral that can supply a useful metal at reasonable cost is called an _____.

7. Most ores are compounds called _____, _____, or _____.

8. The study of taking metals from ores and making them useful is called _____.

9. A scientist who studies metals and ores is called a _____.

REACHING OUT

1. What does *recycle* mean? _____

   _____

2. Why should metals be recycled?

   _____

   _____

Figure E

HOW CAN WE FREE A METAL FROM ITS ORE?

19

roasting: heating an ore in the open air

reducing agent: a material that takes the oxygen out of an ore

coke: a form of carbon

AIM 19 | How can we free a metal from its ore?

Can we use copper ore right out of the ground to make a copper wire? Of course not. A metal must be separated from its ore before it can be used. The method used to separate an ore depends on its chemistry.

First let's look at *oxide* ores. The metal of an oxide ore is combined with *oxygen*. To free the metal we must *reduce* the ore. Reduction removes the oxygen and frees the metal. *Carbon* may be used to reduce an oxide ore. We call the carbon a *reducing agent*. The carbon is heated with the ore.

Let's look at how carbon can reduce copper oxide ore when we heat them together.

OXIDE ORE

REDUCTION	$2CuO +$ C	$\rightarrow$	$2Cu$	$+ CO_2$
	Copper oxide Carbon		Copper (free metal)	Carbon dioxide

In this reaction the carbon and oxygen link up to form carbon dioxide. This sets the copper free.

Metals cannot be freed so easily from sulfide and carbonate ores. It takes two steps: 1. The ores are heated in the open air. This is called *roasting*. Roasting turns the sulfide or carbonate ore into an oxide. 2. Then the oxide can be reduced. The metal is set free. Look at the examples below.

SULFIDE ORE — Copper sulfide

Step 1 ROASTING	$2CuS + 2O_2 \longrightarrow 2CuO + 2SO_2$
	Copper sulfide Oxygen Copper oxide Sulfur dioxide
Step 2 REDUCTION	$2CuO +$ C $\longrightarrow$ $2Cu$ $+ CO_2$
	Copper oxide Carbon Copper (free metal) Carbon dioxide

CARBONATE ORE — Zinc carbonate

Step 1 ROASTING	$ZnCO_3 \longrightarrow ZnO + CO_2$
	Zinc carbonate Zinc oxide Carbon dioxide
Step 2 REDUCTION	$2ZnO +$ C $\longrightarrow$ $2Zn$ $+ CO_2$
	Zinc oxide Carbon Zinc (free metal) Carbon dioxide

NAME _____

120

HOW WE FREE METALS FROM OXIDE ORES

Look at Figures A and B and read the explanations with each. Then answer the questions.

Freeing copper from copper oxide

Figure A shows how copper oxide can be reduced in a laboratory.

1. What ore is being reduced?

   _____

2. What is the reducing agent?

   _____

3. What gas is released?

   _____

4. What metal is freed?

   _____

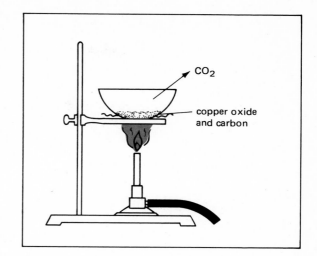

Figure A

Freeing iron from iron oxide

Iron oxide ores are usually reduced in huge *blast furnaces* at high temperatures.

Figure B shows what happens when the iron ore hematite (Fe_2O_3) is reduced.

Follow the decomposition of hematite step by step.

Step 1 Coke (a form of carbon) and hematite are put into the furnace. The coke burns.

$$C + O_2 \longrightarrow CO_2$$

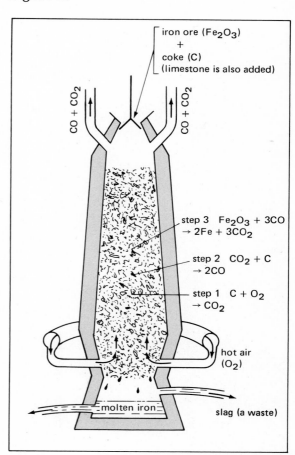

Figure B

5. When coke (carbon) burns, it combines with _____.
   oxygen, carbon dioxide

6. When carbon links up with oxygen it forms _____.
   carbon dioxide, hematite

Step 2   Some of the carbon dioxide and the carbon react together.

$$CO_2 + C \longrightarrow 2CO$$
Carbon monoxide

7. When carbon dioxide and carbon combine they form _____.
oxygen, carbon monoxide

Step 3   The carbon monoxide reacts with the iron oxide.

$$Fe_2O_3 + 3CO \longrightarrow 2Fe + 3CO_2$$

8. What gas does this form?   _____

9. What pure metal is set free?   _____

10. The reducing agent in this reaction is _____.
carbon, carbon dioxide, carbon monoxide

After reduction, molten metal is often poured into molds called *pigs*.

Figure C

NAME _____

HOW WE FREE METALS FROM SULFIDE ORES

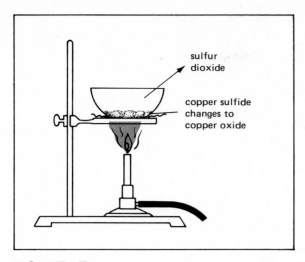

sulfur dioxide

copper sulfide changes to copper oxide

Figure D

Purpose   To free the copper from copper sulfide (CuS)

What You Need   10 grams copper sulfide
powdered charcoal (carbon)
crucible
ring stand
wire gauze
Bunsen burner
Pyrex test tube
hand clamp
long iron wire (or nail)

What To Do

Step 1

1. Place the copper sulfide into the crucible.
2. Heat it with a high flame for about 15 minutes.
3. Stir from time to time with the iron wire.

    The heat causes a chemical reaction. This is the equation:

$$2CuS + 3O_2 \longrightarrow 2CuO + 2SO_2$$

Copper   Oxygen   Copper   Sulfur
sulfide   oxide   dioxide

4. The copper sulfide reacts with _____ from the air.

5. The oxygen _____ the sulfur.
    combines with, replaces

6. The copper sulfide changes to _____.

7. **a)** We smell something like rotten eggs. What gas causes this odor? _____

    b) What happens to this gas? _____

8. What stays behind in the dish? _____

9. Is the copper free? _____

10. What is this first step called? _____

11. One more step is needed to free the copper. What is it called? _____

Step 2

12. Wait for the crucible to cool.

13. Add some of the powdered charcoal to the copper oxide. Mix them.

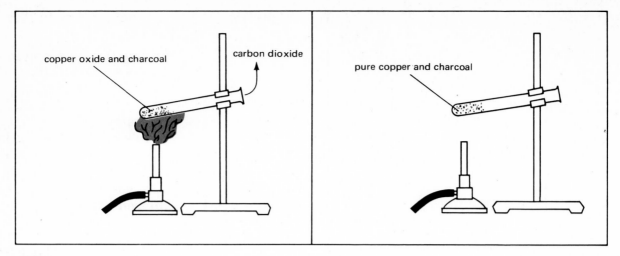

Figure E

14. Place the mixture into the Pyrex test tube. Heat with a high flame.

Another chemical reaction takes place. This is the equation:

$$CuO \quad + \quad C \quad \longrightarrow \quad 2Cu \quad + \quad CO_2$$

Copper oxide   Carbon   Copper   Carbon dioxide

15. The carbon removes the oxygen from the copper oxide. This is called

_____ .

oxidation, reduction

16. With what does the carbon combine? _____

17. What does the linkup of the carbon and oxygen form? _____

18. What is left behind? _____

19. The first step in freeing a metal from a sulfide ore is called *roasting*. What is this

second step called? _____

HOW WE FREE METALS FROM CARBONATE ORES

Purpose   To free lead from lead carbonate ($PbCO_3$)

What You Need

Use the same equipment you used in the previous experiment with one exception. Instead of 10 grams of copper sulfide, use 10 grams of lead carbonate.

NAME _____

What To Do

Step 1

1. Place the lead carbonate into the crucible. Heat it with a high flame for about 15 minutes.

2. Stir from time to time with the wire.

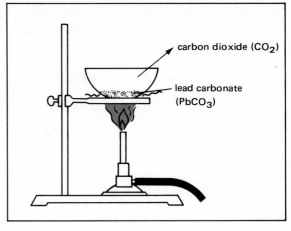

Figure F

The heat causes a chemical reaction. This is the equation:

$$PbCO_3 \xrightarrow{\text{heat}} PbO + CO_2$$

Lead carbonate   Lead oxide   Carbon dioxide

3. The lead carbonate _____ .

oxidizes, reduces, decomposes

4. Heat decomposes lead carbonate to _____ and _____ .

5. What happens to the carbon dioxide? _____

6. What happens to the lead oxide? _____

7. This first step in the freeing of a metal from a carbonate is called _____ .

Step 2

8. Wait for the crucible to cool.

9. Add some of the powdered charcoal to the lead oxide. Mix.

10. Place the mixture into the test tube. Heat it with a high flame.

Figure G

Another chemical reaction takes place. This is the equation:

$$2PbO + C \longrightarrow CO_2 + 2Pb$$

Lead oxide   Carbon   Carbon dioxide   Lead

11. The carbon removes the oxygen from the lead oxide. What is this process called?

_____

12. With what does the carbon combine? _____

13. The linkup of carbon and oxygen forms _____ .

14. What is left behind? _____

15. Two steps are needed to free a metal from a carbonate ore. Name them in order.

_____ _____

125

MATCHING

Match the two lists. Write the correct letter on the line next to each number.

1. _____ roasting

2. _____ roasting and reduction

3. _____ reducing agent

4. _____ CO

5. _____ CO_2

a) steps in separating sulfide and carbonate ores

b) removes oxygen from a compound

c) forms when carbon and CO_2 combine

d) heating an ore in the open air

e) carbon dioxide

WORD SEARCH

The words in this list are hidden in the groups of letters. Try to find each word. Draw a line around each word. The spelling may go in any direction: up-and-down, across, or diagonally.

REPLACEMENT
SINGLE
DOUBLE
OXIDATION
SLOW
RAPID
BURN
ORE
MINERAL
METAL
OXIDE
SULFIDE
IRON
ZINC

X	O	R	E	O	R	A	I	B
E	X	L	A	R	E	N	I	M
D	I	W	D	I	P	A	R	Z
I	D	O	U	B	L	E	I	I
X	A	L	U	E	A	N	C	E
O	T	S	L	O	C	O	M	D
S	I	N	G	L	E	G	N	I
S	O	U	B	R	M	Q	R	F
O	N	N	C	D	E	O	W	L
R	I	B	U	R	N	S	L	U
M	M	B	L	A	T	E	M	S

NAME _____

WHAT IS AN ALLOY?

20

alloy: a blend of metals

AIM 20 | What is an alloy?

All metals share certain properties. But no two metals have exactly the same properties. For example, some are lighter or stronger than others. Some shine more. Some melt more easily or conduct electricity better than others.

Often, a manufacturer wants to use a certain metal. It has all the properties that are needed—except one. For example, the metal may be strong enough, but it rusts easily. What can be done?

METALLURGISTS TO THE RESCUE!

Metallurgists have learned to "custom-make" metals. They mix and blend two or more metals. This mixing changes certain properties.

A mixture of metals that acts as a single metal is called an *alloy. Stainless steel* and *Duralumin* are examples of alloys.

■ Iron rusts easily. But *stainless steel* does not. Stainless steel is an alloy of iron, chromium, nickel, and a small amount of carbon.

■ Aluminum is light. But it is not strong. *Duralumin* is an alloy of aluminum, copper, magnesium, and manganese. Duralumin is light *and* strong—about as strong as steel. It is used in airplanes. Some automobile engines are made of this tough alloy.

Your dentist fills cavities with an alloy of mercury and some other metal. The "other" metal may be copper, tin, lead, zinc, or silver. The alloy starts out like a sticky putty. It slowly hardens after it is mixed. Why do you think your dentist tells you, "Don't eat on that side for at least one hour"?

There are thousands of alloys. New alloys are being discovered all the time.

Most metal products we use are not pure metals. They are alloys.

NAME _____

SOME COMMON ALLOYS

Figure A

Figure B

Nichrome [NIE krome] is an alloy of nickel, chromium, iron, and manganese. Nichrome wire has a high electrical resistance. It gives off a great deal of heat when electricity moves through it.

The heating elements of electric irons and toasters are made of nichrome.

Any steel is an alloy. It is very strong. If vanadium is added to steel, the steel becomes even stronger.

Automobile frames, gears, springs, and axles are made of *vanadium steel.*

Solder [SOD er] is an alloy. There are many kinds of solder. One common solder is a blend of tin and lead. Solder melts easily and can join two pieces of metal together.

Figure C

Figure D

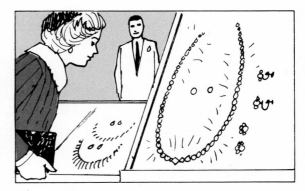

Figure E

Chromium steel has great hardness. It is used in making bank vaults, special tools, and armor plate.

Costume jewelry is rarely pure gold or pure silver. It is made of an alloy. A small amount of cheap metal is added to the gold or silver. This addition serves two purposes: it lessens the cost, and it makes the gold or silver harder.

Figure F

The earliest alloy was *bronze*. Bronze is a blend of copper and tin. It was discovered (probably by accident) about 5,000 years ago.

Bronze is very hard and durable. It was widely used for knives, spearheads, battle axes, helmets, shields, and swords. Early cups and vases were also made of bronze.

Today, bronze is used for things like statues, coins, and lamps. Our "copper" penny is really a bronze alloy.

COMPLETING SENTENCES

Complete the sentences with the choices below.

___

strong	alloy	metals
alloys	same	special
custom-made	melted together	metallurgists
lightness		

1. All metals have certain properties that are the _____.

2. Every metal has certain _____ properties.

3. A special property of aluminum is its _____.

4. Aluminum is not very _____.

5. Aluminum can be made stronger when it is mixed with certain other

_____.

NAME _____

6. A mixture of metals that acts as a single metal is called an _____.

7. An alloy can be called a "_____" metal.

8. The metals of most alloys are _____.

9. "Recipes" for alloys are figured out by _____.

10. Most metal products we use are _____.

MATCHING   Match the two lists. Write the correct letter on the line next to each number.

1. _____ alloy

2. _____ stainless steel

3. _____ Duralumin

4. _____ bronze

5. _____ iron

a) non-rusting iron alloy

b) rusts

c) first alloy

d) any blend of metals

e) light and strong

MAKING WOOD'S METAL

Figure G

Wood's metal is an alloy of bismuth, cadmium, tin, and lead. It melts at a low temperature—70°C (158°F). This is lower than the boiling point of water. Wood's metal is used as "plugs" in automatic fire sprinklers. Heat from a fire quickly melts this metal, and the water sprinkles out. Why not make your own alloy?

What You Need

crucible
tripod
Bunsen burner
iron wire (or nail)
metal tongs
asbestos pad
Pyrex beaker
bismuth—20 grams
lead—10 grams
tin—5 grams
cadmium—5 grams

How To Do the Experiment

Figure H

1. Place the metals into the crucible. Leave out just a few "sprinkles" of each metal.

2. Heat the crucible. Stir the metals with the iron wire until the mixture is melted.

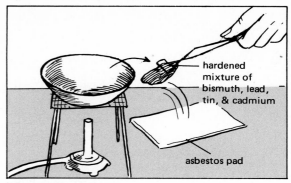

Figure I

3. Remove the crucible with the tongs. Place it on the asbestos pad. Let the mixture cool and harden.

Figure J

4. Boil some water in the beaker.

5. One at a time, sprinkle the separate metals into the boiling water. Notice what happens.

Figure K

6. Pry the hardened metal from the crucible. Drop it carefully into the boiling water. (DON'T SPLASH!)

What You Saw and Learned

7. The *separate* metals _____ melt when you sprinkled them in
   <u>did, did not</u>
   boiling water. But the *hardened* mixture _____ melt.
   <u>did, did not</u>

8. **a)** The hardened mixture_____ an alloy.
   <u>is, is not</u>

   b) What is its name? _____

9. Wood's metal melts at a _____ temperature than the metals that
   <u>higher, lower</u>
   make it up.

NAME _____

WHAT IS METAL ACTIVITY?

21

Table of Metal Activity: a list of metals in the order of their activity

AIM 21 | What is metal activity?

You have seen rusted iron. But you have never seen rusted gold. Gold does not rust. It keeps its shine year after year—century after century.

Iron forms compounds. So does gold. But iron forms compounds more easily than gold does. We say that iron is *more active* than gold.

Different metals have different activities. Let's compare aluminum and sodium.

If you drop a piece of aluminum into cold water, nothing happens. There is no reaction. If you drop a piece of *sodium* into cold water, it's a different story! The sodium and water react *immediately*. The sodium races across the surface of the water. Sometimes the sodium seems to burn with a yellow flame. It's easy to see that sodium is *more active* than aluminum.

If you drop a piece of potassium into the water, the reaction is even *more* violent. Potassium is even more active than sodium. The potassium races across the water even faster. And it always seems to burn with a violet flame.

In these reactions, the *more active* sodium and potassium *replace* the *less active* hydrogen of the water. This is the equation for the sodium/water reaction.

$$2\,Na + 2\,HOH \longrightarrow 2\,NaOH + H_2$$

The more active sodium replaces   the less active hydrogen . . .   and sets it free.

In any replacement reaction, a *more* active metal replaces a *less* active metal.

Chemists know how active each metal is. The table on the next page lists the metals in the order of their activity.

This table lets us predict many chemical reactions.

NAME _____

UNDERSTANDING METAL ACTIVITY

A table of metal activity is shown on the right. It lists the metals according to their activity. Study the table. Then answer the questions.

MORE ACTIVE ←	Lithium	Li	LESS ACTIVE →
	Potassium	K	
	Barium	Ba	
	Calcium	Ca	
	Sodium	Na	
	Magnesium	Mg	
	Aluminum	Al	
	Zinc	Zn	
	Iron	Fe	
	Tin	Sn	
	Lead	Pb	
	Hydrogen*	H	
	Copper	Cu	
	Mercury	Hg	
	Silver	Ag	
	Platinum	Pt	
	Gold	Au	

1. Which is the *most* active metal?

   _____

2. Which is the *least* active metal?

   _____

3. Which is correct? (Circle the letter of the correct answer.)
   a) A *less* active metal can replace a *more* active metal.

   b) A *more* active metal can replace a *less* active metal.

4. Which is *more* active,
   a) sodium or iron? _____
   b) tin or lead? _____
   c) gold or silver? _____
   d) tin or aluminum? _____

5. Which is *less* active,
   a) sodium or calcium? _____
   b) zinc or tin? _____
   c) copper or mercury? _____
   d) hydrogen or platinum? _____

6. Name the metals that *can* replace *calcium*. _____

   _____

7. Name the metals that *cannot* replace *mercury*. _____

   _____

8. Which is the only metal that can replace potassium? _____

9. a) Can any metal replace lithium? _____

   b) Why or why not? _____

10. a) Can gold replace any metal? _____

    b) Why or why not? _____

_____

*Hydrogen is included for reference.

TESTING METAL ACTIVITY BETWEEN COPPER AND IRON

Figure A

What You Need

strip of copper
iron sulfate solution
beaker

How To Do the Test

1. Place the copper strip into the iron sulfate solution.

2. Wait 3 to 4 minutes. Then remove the copper strip.

   Examine it carefully.

What You Saw and Learned

3. **a)** Did the strip change color? _____

   b) Did the solution change color? _____

4. A chemical reaction _____ take place.
   _{did, did not} (did, did not)

5. The copper _____ become coated with iron.
   (did, did not)

6. The copper _____ replace the iron of the iron sulfate.
   (did, did not)

7. **a)** Which is *less* active, iron or copper? (Check the table.) _____

   b) Which is *more* active, iron or copper? _____

   Can a *less* active metal replace a *more* active metal? _____

8. Why didn't the copper replace the iron? _____

9. **a)** Can a chemical equation show what happened? _____

   b) Why or why not? _____

NAME _____

TESTING METAL ACTIVITY BETWEEN IRON AND COPPER SULFATE

What You Need   beaker
                    iron nail
                    copper sulfate solution

What You Need To Know

- Iron is *silver* in color.

- Iron sulfate is *green.*

How To Do the Test

1. Place the nail into the copper sulfate solution.

2. Wait 3 to 4 minutes. Then remove the nail. Examine the nail and the solution.

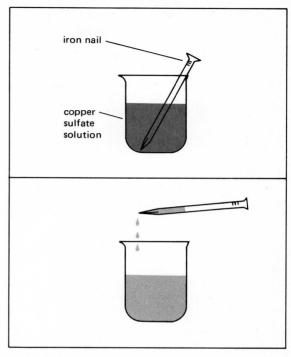

Figure B

What You Saw and Learned

3. a) Did the *nail* change color? _____ **b)** What color? _____

4. a) Did the *solution* change color? _____ **b)** What color? _____

5. A chemical reaction _____ take place.

                                        _{did, did not}

The following equation shows what happened:

$$Fe + CuSO_4 \longrightarrow Cu + FeSO_4$$

Iron   Copper sulfate   Copper   Iron sulfate

6. Which is correct? (Circle the letter of the correct answer.)
   a) The iron replaced the copper.
   b) The copper replaced the iron.

7. a) Which is *more* active, iron or copper? (Look at the table.)

   b) Which is less active, iron or copper? _____

8. Why did the iron replace the copper? _____

9. a) Which metal did the reaction set free? _____

   b) What happened to it? _____

10. Why did the solution turn green? _____

COMPLETING SENTENCES

Complete the sentences with the choices below. One of these is used twice.

more   lithium   gold
compounds   less

1. By metal "activity" we mean how easily a metal forms _____.

2. The *most* active metal is _____.

3. The *least* active metal is _____.

4. A _____ active metal will replace a _____ active metal.

5. The *higher* a metal is on the activity table, the _____ active it is.

PREDICTING REACTIONS

Which of these will result in a chemical reaction? Which will not? Mark a check (√) in the correct box.

		Chemical reaction *will* take place	Chemical reaction will *not* take place
1.	Cu + AgNO$_3$		
2.	Ba + Zn(NO$_3$)$_2$		
3.	Ag + Cu(NO$_3$)$_2$		
4.	Au + Pb(NO$_3$)$_2$		
5.	Mg + H$_2$SO$_4$		
6.	Hg + H$_2$SO$_4$		
7.	Mg + HOH		
8.	Fe + Zn(NO$_3$)$_2$		

REACHING OUT

Check the activity table and the Periodic Table (pages 168–169). Which metals are more active, those on the right or those on the left of the Periodic Table?

_____

NAME _____

138

WHAT IS CORROSION?

corrosion: the slow wearing away of a metal by chemical action

tarnish: a form of corrosion

galvanize: to coat with melted tin

AIM 22 | What is corrosion?

How often have you seen rust? You don't have to look very far to see it. Just find a car a few years old. Chances are that it has some rust spots.

Car bodies are made of iron. Iron is silver-gray in color. When iron rusts, it turns reddish-brown. Rust flakes off easily. Then fresh iron beneath it rusts and flakes away. Little by little, the entire piece of metal rusts away.

Rusting is an example of *corrosion*. Corrosion is the gradual wearing away of metal by *chemical* action.

The chief cause of corrosion is the *oxygen* in the air. Other gases that cause corrosion are *carbon dioxide* and *hydrogen sulfide.*

■ Metals like *iron, aluminum,* and *nickel* are corroded by oxygen.

■ The main causes of *copper* corrosion are carbon dioxide and water vapor. Copper also reacts with hydrogen sulfide. The burning of fuels like coal and natural gas puts hydrogen sulfide into the air. Corrosion changes copper from reddish-orange to *green.*

■ Another metal that reacts with hydrogen sulfide is *silver.* Corroded, or *tarnished,* silver is black.

Corrosion takes away the shiny luster of metal. But sometimes it may be helpful to the life of the metal.

For example, corroded aluminum (aluminum oxide) does not flake off like rust does. It *clings* to the aluminum and keeps the air away. The corrosion actually forms a protective covering. It stops further corrosion.

Several other metals form protective coats. Copper, zinc, and silver are among them.

Sometimes we may want to prevent corrosion altogether on certain metal objects. This may be done by coating the metal. Such things as paint, lacquer, grease, or even another metal may be used to give the object protection against corrosion.

NAME _____

UNDERSTANDING CORROSION

silver tarnish (Ag_2S)

Figure A

Look at Figures A, B, and C. Then answer the questions with each.

Figure A shows silver that has been tarnished. This is the equation for the corrosion of silver.

$$4Ag + 2H_2S \longrightarrow 2Ag_2S + 2H_2$$

1. **a)** What causes silver to corrode (tarnish)? _____

    b) What puts this gas into the air?

    _____

2. What is the chemical name of tarnished silver? _____
    (Figure it out from the formula.)

3. Does silver tarnish protect the silver from further corrosion? _____

Figure B

The Statue of Liberty has been standing in New York harbor since 1886.

When it was new, the statue was reddish-orange in color. Now it is green. Corrosion made it turn color.

4. **a)** What metal covers the Statue of Liberty? _____

    b) What caused it to corrode?

    _____

5. **a)** Will the corrosion continue?

    _____

    b) Why or why not? _____

    _____

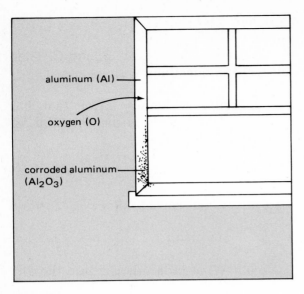

Figure C

Figure C shows corroded aluminum.

This is the equation for the corrosion of aluminum:

$$4Al + 3O_2 \longrightarrow 2Al_2O_3$$

Aluminum oxide

6. What causes aluminum to corrode?

   _____

7. What is the name of the corroded

   aluminum? _____

8. Does the aluminum oxide protect the aluminum from further corrosion? _____

HOW DOES SULFUR AFFECT SILVER?

What You Need To Know

Silver reacts with many sulfur compounds. Egg white contains sulfur.

What You Need

hard-boiled egg white
shiny silver spoon

How To Do the Experiment

1. Push the silver spoon into the hard-boiled egg white.

2. Keep it there for about 10 minutes. Then remove it. Compare the part that was inside the egg to the part that was not.

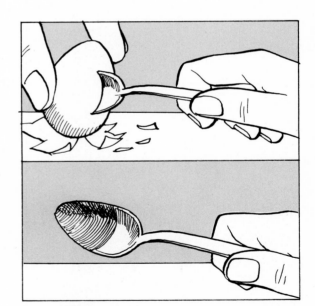

Figure D

What You Saw and Learned

3. The silver that was in the egg white _____.

   turned green, turned black, stayed the same

4. The silver _____ corrode.

   did, did not

5. What substance corrodes silver? _____

NAME _____

SOME WAYS OF PREVENTING CORROSION

Figure E

Coating metal with paint or lacquer prevents corrosion.

Some protective paint jobs are *huge*. Take the George Washington Bridge, for example. It takes 25 workers four years and 45,500 liters (12,000 gallons) of paint to cover this structure!

Repainting is done every four to nine years.

Figure F

Figure G

Garbage pails, rain pipes, water pipes, and nails are some *galvanized* products. Galvanizing means dipping metal objects into molten *zinc*. Galvanizing protects. But it doesn't last forever. It wears off in time.

A "tin" can is really steel *coated* with tin.

Coating steel with molten zinc or tin is done by a process called `hot-dipping.*

HOW CAN WE PREVENT CORROSION?

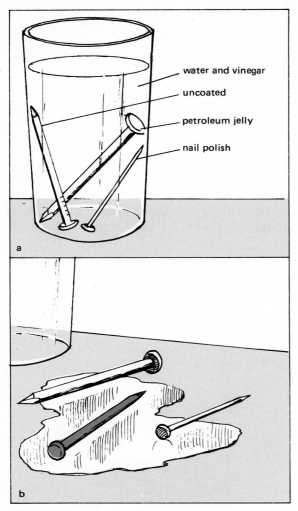

water and vinegar
uncoated
petroleum jelly
nail polish

a

b

Figure H

Rusting is a form of corrosion that we all know. This is the formula for rusting:

$$4Fe + 3O_2 \longrightarrow 2Fe_2O_3$$

Iron oxide

Can we prevent iron from rusting?

What You Need To Know

- Iron rusts in water.

- Vinegar, when added to water, speeds the rusting.

What You Need

3 iron nails
petroleum jelly
clear nail polish (lacquer)
clear water
vinegar
drinking glass

How To Do the Experiment

1. Fill the glass ¾ full with water. Add a little vinegar and stir.

2. Coat one nail with the clear nail polish. Let it dry.

3. Coat another nail with a thin layer of petroleum jelly.

4. Do not coat the third nail.

5. Drop the three nails into the glass. Let them stand overnight. Remove them the next day. Examine each nail.

What You Saw and Learned

6. The uncoated nail _____ rust.
   did, did not

7. The coated nails _____ rust.
   did, did not

8. Name two coatings that protect against corrosion. _____ _____

9. Name some other ways to protect metal from corrosion. _____

_____

NAME _____

COMPLETING SENTENCES

Complete the sentences with the choices below.

tarnish	tin	zinc
oxygen	carbon dioxide	grease
aluminum oxide	corrosion	metal
rust	iron oxide	paint
hydrogen sulfide	prevent	

1. The gradual wearing away of metal by chemical action is called _____ _____.

2. Most corrosion is caused by the _____ in the air.

3. Other gases that cause corrosion are _____ and _____.

4. The most common form of corrosion is _____.

5. The chemical name for rust is _____.

6. Sulfur and hydrogen sulfide cause silver to _____.

7. The chemical name for corroded aluminum is _____.

8. The corroded aluminum helps _____ further corrosion.

9. We can prevent corrosion by coating metals with _____, _____, or even another _____.

10. Two metals that are used to give a protective coat are _____ and _____.

MATCHING

Match the two lists. Write the correct letter on the line next to each number.

1. _____ oxygen   a) silver corrosion

2. _____ rust   b) coated with zinc

3. _____ tarnish   c) iron oxide

4. _____ galvanized   d) chief cause of corrosion

5. _____ corrosion   e) any slow wearing away of metal

Write T on the line next to the number if the sentence is true. Write F if the sentence is false.

1. _____ Corrosion builds metals.

2. _____ All metals corrode.

3. _____ Most metals corrode.

4. _____ Only oxygen causes corrosion.

5. _____ Oxygen causes most corrosion.

6. _____ Iron can rust.

7. _____ Rust protects iron from further corrosion.

8. _____ Aluminum oxide protects aluminum from further corrosion.

9. _____ Carbon dioxide tarnishes silver.

10. _____ Zinc and tin tarnish easily.

WORD SCRAMBLE Unscramble each of the following to form a word or term that you have read in this book.

1. THRAINS _____

2. DOORCER _____

3. IVATTICY _____

4. LOYAL _____

REACHING OUT

1. You notice a rust spot on a piece of iron. You plan to paint it.

   What should you do before you paint the rust spot? _____

   Why? _____

   _____

2. In what kind of climate does corrosion take place the fastest? _____

   _____

NAME _____

HOW DO WE ELECTROPLATE METALS?

23

electroplate: to coat with a metal by using electricity

Many metals aren't what they seem to be. They are *plated*. Plating places a thin layer of one metal upon another metal. Some metals are plated by hot-dipping. Most metals, however, are plated by *electroplating*.

Electroplating protects metals. It also makes metals look better. Most electroplated metals are bright and shiny.

Automobile bumpers, for example, are made of steel. Steel is not very shiny. Bumpers are electroplated with *chromium*. Chromium gives the bumpers a bright shine. It also protects the steel from rusting.

Electroplating is often used only for appearance. Gold and silver are attractive, but expensive, metals. Many pieces of "gold" and "silver" jewelry are really mostly cheap metal. They are just electroplated with gold or silver.

Electroplating is easy to do. It is explained below. Check with Figure A, on the facing page, as you read.

1. Electroplating is done in a liquid *salt solution*. There are many kinds of salts. The salt you use must contain the metal you want to deposit. For example, if you want to plate a metal with silver, you use a salt like *silver nitrate* ($AgNO_3$).

2. Connect the metal you want to *deposit* (such as silver) to the *anode*. The anode is the positive (+) electric pole.

3. Connect the metal you want to coat to the *cathode*. The cathode is the negative (−) electric pole.

4. Pass a weak *direct* electrical current through the solution.

The metal you wanted to coat becomes plated with the metal of the salt solution. In our example, that metal is silver.

The thickness of the plate depends upon how long the electricity flows. The longer it flows, the thicker the plate becomes. But even a "thick" plate is very thin.

NAME _____

UNDERSTANDING ELECTROPLATING

Look at Figures A and B. Then answer the questions or fill in the blanks.

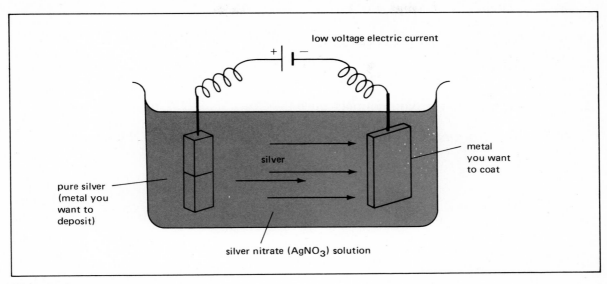

Figure A

1. Electroplating is done _____.
   <u>in air, in a liquid solution</u>

2. The solution used in electroplating contains a dissolved _____.
   <u>salt, gas</u>

3. The salt of an electroplating solution must contain the metal

   _____.
   <u>you are coating, you want to deposit</u>

4. **a)** Silver nitrate solution can deposit the metal _____.

   b) Copper sulfate can deposit the metal _____.

   c) Gold cyanide can deposit the metal _____.

5. Electroplating uses _____ current.
   <u>strong direct, weak direct, weak alternating</u>

6. Electricity has two poles: *positive* and *negative*.

   a) The *positive* pole is called the _____.
   <u>anode, cathode</u>

   b) The *negative* pole is called the _____.
   <u>anode, cathode</u>

Circle the letter of your answer.

7. In electroplating, what do you connect to the anode?
   a) the metal you want *to* be coated.
   b) the metal you want *as* a coating.

8. What do you connect to the cathode?
   a) the metal you want to give coating to.
   b) the metal you want to use as a coating.

9. a) To deposit silver, you connect pure _____ to the anode.

   b) To deposit nickel, you connect pure _____ to the anode.

You can electroplate *without* a pure metal connected to the anode. You can use just the salt solution.

For example, let's look at our silver-plating setup but with one change.

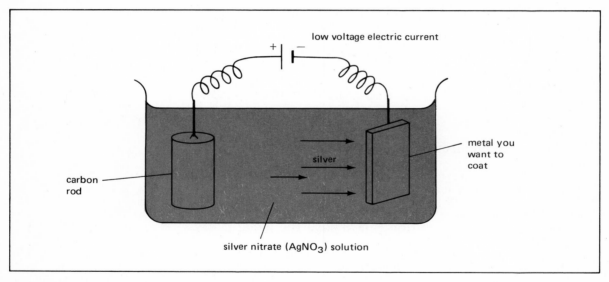

Figure B

A plain carbon rod has taken the place of the silver. The silver plate comes from the silver nitrate solution *only*.

10. Plating this way can produce only a thin coat, or can coat only a few pieces. Why?

_____

_____

NAME _____

IDENTIFYING PARTS IN ELECTROPLATING

Four electroplating setups are shown in Figures C through F. One part of each setup is labeled. Two parts are not labeled. Identify the parts that are not labeled. Write your answers on the lines under each diagram. (Hint: Check terminals carefully!) Choose from the following:

gold cyanide solution

zinc coat

pure nickel

nickel coat

tin coat

pure gold

zinc chloride solution

pure tin

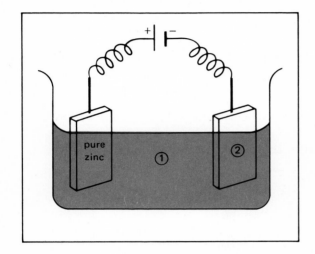

Figure C

1. _____

2. _____

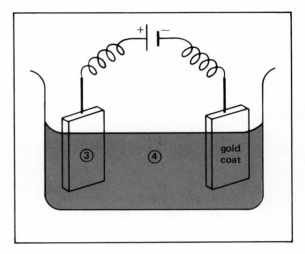

Figure D

3. _____

4. _____

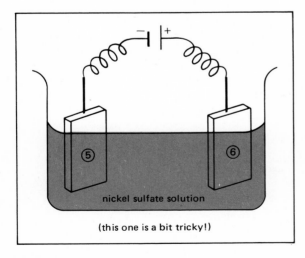

(this one is a bit tricky!)

Figure E

5. _____

6. _____

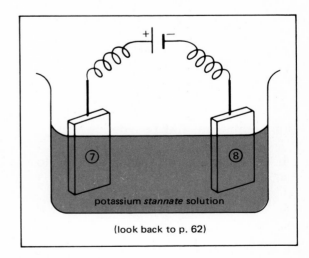

(look back to p. 62)

Figure F

7. _____

8. _____

EXPERIMENTING WITH ELECTROPLATING

What You Need To Know

- The color of carbon is *black.*
- The color of iron is *silver-gray.*
- The color of copper is *reddish-orange.*

What You Need   glass beaker   two dry cells
                     copper sulfate solution   wire
                     two metal clips   switch
                     one carbon rod   file
                     one clean iron nail

How To Do the Experiment

1. Set up the materials as in Figure G.

2. Pass electricity through the solution for about 5 minutes. Then open the switch.

3. Remove the carbon rod and nail. Examine them.

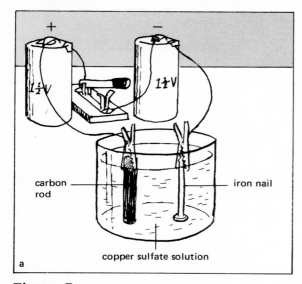

Figure G

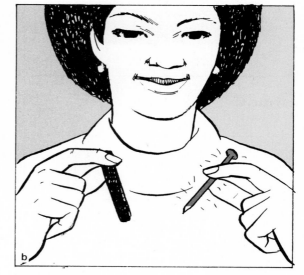

Figure H

What You Saw and Learned

4. The carbon rod was connected to the _____.

anode, cathode

5. The iron nail was connected to the _____.

anode, cathode

6. **a)** Which became plated, the carbon or the iron? _____

    b) How do you know? _____

NAME _____

7. a) What color is the plate? _____

    b) What metal is the plate? _____

    c) Where did the plate metal come from? _____

    NOW *gently* file the head of the nail.

8. a) The plating _____ file off easily.
    did, did not

    b) This shows that the plating is _____.
    thick, thin

9. If you pass the electricity through the solution longer, the plate becomes

    _____.
    thicker, thinner

10. If you wish to coat many pieces, what must you connect to the anode?

    _____

COMPLETING SENTENCES Complete the sentences with the choices below.

---

negative	look better	hot-dipping
weak	replaces	positive
plate	thin	electroplating
protects	salt solution	

1. *Plating* places a _____ layer of one metal upon another metal.

2. Some plating, like tinning and galvanizing, is done by _____.

3. Plating that uses electricity is called _____.

4. Electroplating is done with _____ direct electrical current.

5. Electroplating _____ metals. Electroplating also makes metals

    _____.

6. Electroplating is done in a _____.

7. The salt you use in electroplating must contain the metal you wish as the

    _____.

8. The metal you want to cover is connected to the _____ electrical pole.

9. The pure metal you want as the plating is connected to the _____ pole.

10. The pure metal _____ the metal from the solution that is used up.

153

REACHING OUT

In solution, a salt breaks up into *ions*. An ion, you remember, has a charge.

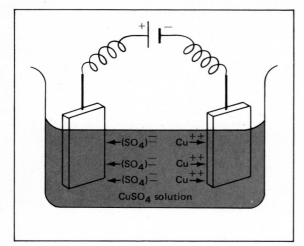

Figure I

For example, in solution, copper sulfate ($CuSO_4$) breaks up into:

- *positively* charged *copper* ions (Cu^{+2}), and
- *negatively* charged *sulfate* ions (SO_4^{-2}).

The copper ions move towards the *negative* pole. The sulfate ions move towards the *positive* pole.

a) Why do the ions move towards these poles? _____

_____

A plus ion is an atom that has lost one or more of its electrons.

b) In copper sulfate, how many electrons has each copper ion lost? _____

c) Where do the copper ions pick up these electrons again? _____

_____

d) What does each copper ion become when it picks up the electrons it had lost?

_____

WHAT IS HARD WATER?

24

distilled water: pure water with no minerals dissolved in it

hard water: water containing certain dissolved mineral salts; hard water does not lather easily

soft water: water that does not contain the dissolved salts found in hard water; soft water lathers easily

The water you drink is safe but it is not "pure." "Pure" water has nothing dissolved in it. Tap water has mineral salts dissolved in it. Rainwater picks up these mineral salts from the ground.

There are many kinds of mineral salts. Water that contains dissolved salts of *calcium, magnesium,* or *iron* is called *hard* water. Hard water is hard to lather. You need a lot of soap to work up even a small lather. It wastes money, time, and energy.

There are two kinds of hard water—*temporary* and *permanent.*

TEMPORARY HARD WATER *Temporary* hard water contains either *calcium bicarbonate, magnesium bicarbonate,* or *iron bicarbonate.*

Temporary hard water can be "softened" by *boiling.* Heat decomposes bicarbonate salts. They change to *carbonate* salts. Carbonate salts do not dissolve in water. They settle to the bottom of their containers.

Another way to soften temporary hard water is by the use of chemical softeners. *Washing soda, borax,* and *slaked lime* are common chemical water softeners.

PERMANENT HARD WATER *Permanent* hard water contains *chloride* or *sulfate* salts. It cannot be softened by boiling. Permanent hard water is softened with a chemical softener.

Hard water is a nuisance. It can also be a big problem. The deposit of carbonate salts can clog steam pipes, hot water pipes, and boilers.

Also, dissolved iron can stain sinks and fabrics.

NAME _____

SOFT AND HARD WATER

Study Figures A and B. Then answer the questions.

Figure A   **Figure B**

1. "Hard" water is being used in Figure _____ .

A, B

2. Hard water _____ lather easily.

does, does not

3. Hard water contains dissolved salts of three metals. Name these metals.

   _____   _____   _____

4. *Temporary* hard water contains dissolved _____ salts.

bicarbonate, chloride or sulfate

5. *Permanent* hard water contains dissolved _____ salts.

carbonate, chloride or sulfate

   Circle the letter of the correct answer.

6. *Temporary* hard water can be softened by
   a) adding a chemical softener
   b) boiling
   c) both a and b

7. *Permanent* hard water can be softened by
   a) adding a chemical softener
   b) boiling
   c) both a and b

8. Name three chemical water softeners. _____ _____

   _____

157

THE DISADVANTAGES OF HARD WATER

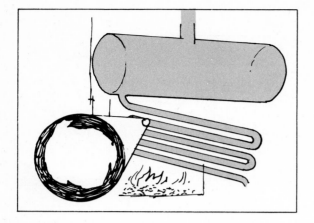

Figure C

Calcium carbonate deposit is called scale. These are examples of scale inside of boiler pipes.

Scale cuts the flow of water. In time, what will happen to these pipes?

_____

Figure D

Many people in hard-water areas use *soapless detergents*. Soapless detergents work well in both soft and hard water.

Do you live in a soft-water area or

a hard-water area? _____

_____

Figure E

Water is used in making textiles. Hard water can discolor fabrics.

Fabric manufacturers in hard-water areas add chemical softeners to their water.

SOFTENING HARD WATER

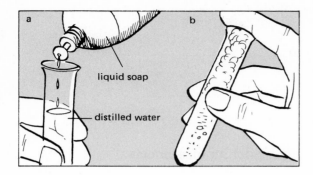

Figure F

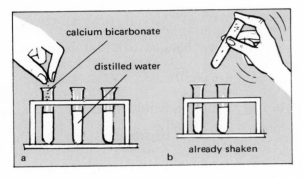

Figure G

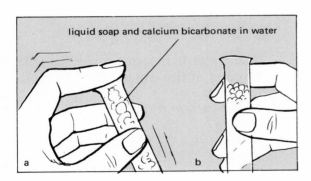

Figure H

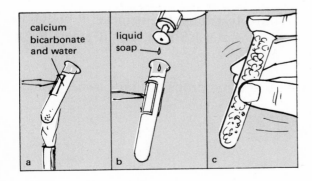

Figure I

Step 1

- Half fill a test tube with *distilled water.*

- Add three drops of liquid *soap.* Shake.

1. The water _____ lather easily.
   <small>does, does not</small>

2. Distilled water is _____ water.
   <small>hard, soft</small>

3. Distilled water _____ contain dissolved salts.
   <small>does, does not</small>

Step 2

- Half-fill three test tubes with distilled water.
- Add a pinch of *calcium bicarbonate* to each test tube. Shake.

4. The calcium bicarbonate _____ dissolve in the water.
   <small>does, does not</small>

Step 3

- Add three drops of liquid soap to one of the test tubes. Shake.

5. The water _____ lather easily.
   <small>does, does not</small>

6. Water with a dissolved bicarbonate salt is _____ water.
   <small>hard, soft</small>

Step 4

- Boil the mixture in the second test tube. (Remember, it contains hard water.) Allow it to cool.

- Add three drops of liquid *soap.* Shake.

7. a) The water now _____ lather easily.
　　　　　　　　　　　　　does, does not

b) The water is now _____ water.
　　　　　　　　　　　　hard, soft

8. a) Water with a dissolved bicarbonate salt is _____ hard water.
　　　　　　　　　　　　　　　　　　　　　　　　temporary, permanent

b) Why? _____

The equation below shows how heat changes calcium bicarbonate:

$$Ca(HCO_3)_2 \text{ (dissolved in water)} \xrightarrow{\text{heat}} CaCO_3 + CO_2 + H_2O$$

Calcium　　　　　　　　　　　　　　　　　Calcium　　Carbon　　Water
bicarbonate　　　　　　　　　　　　　　　carbonate　dioxide

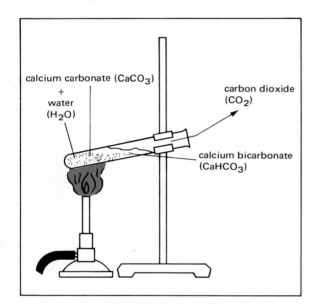

Figure J

9. Boiling changes calcium *bi*carbonate to calcium _____.

10. a) Calcium carbonate _____ dissolve in water.
　　　　　　　　　　　　　　　　does, does not

b) What happens to the calcium carbonate? _____
_____

11. The water that forms mixed in with the rest of the water. What happens to the carbon dioxide? _____
_____

Step 5

- Sprinkle some *washing soda* into the third test tube. (Remember, it contains hard water.) Shake. Let it stand for a minute.

- Add three drops of liquid *soap*. Shake.

Figure K

NAME _____

160

12. The water _____ lather easily.

does, does not

13. The water is now _____ water.

hard, soft

14. What changed the hard water to soft water? _____

15. Washing soda "softens" hard water. Name two other water softeners.

_____ _____

16. Water softeners can soften *temporary* hard water. Can water softeners soften *permanent* hard water? _____

17. Temporary hard water can be softened by boiling. Can *permanent* hard water be softened by boiling? _____

18. *Temporary* hard water contains _____ salts.

bicarbonate, chloride or sulfate

19. *Permanent* hard water contains _____ salts.

bicarbonate, chloride or sulfate

20. Name the three *metals* (elements) found in hard water. _____

_____ _____

MINERAL SALTS AND HARD WATER

Six salts are listed below. Fill in the spaces next to each salt with the correct information. The first line has been done for you.

	Salt	Produces temporary *hard* water or permanent *hard* water?	Water softened by boiling	Water softened with a water softener
1.	Magnesium sulfate		*no*	*yes*
2.	Calcium chloride			
3.	Magnesium bicarbonate			
4.	Iron sulfate			
5.	Calcium bicarbonate			
6.	Iron chloride			

COMPLETING SENTENCES

Complete the sentences with the choices below. One of these may be used twice.

ground	hard water	chemical softener
borax	salts	temporary
permanent	boiling	hot water pipes
slaked lime	scale	sulfate
chloride	bicarbonate	washing soda

1. Tap water has mineral _____ dissolved in it.

2. Rainwater picks up mineral salts from the _____.

3. Water that contains calcium, magnesium, or iron salts is called _____.

4. There are two kinds of hard water. They are _____ and _____ hard water.

5. Temporary hard water contains _____ salts.

6. Permanent hard water contains _____ or _____ salts.

7. Temporary hard water can be softened by _____ or by adding a _____.

8. Permanent hard water cannot be softened by _____.

9. Three chemical water softeners are _____, _____, and _____.

10. Carbonate deposits are called _____. These deposits can clog _____.

WORD SCRAMBLE

Unscramble each of the following to form a word or term that you have read in this book.

1. RABBITCANOE   _____

2. DOTEACH   _____

3. LASEC   _____

4. CREEPTALLOTE   _____

NAME _____

HOW ARE METALS IMPORTANT TO LIFE AND HEALTH?

25

chlorophyll: important compound that contains magnesium, found in green plants

hemoglobin: important compound that contains iron, found in blood

trace amounts: small amounts

AIM 25 | How are metals important to life and health?

There can be no life without metals. Metals are part of all living matter.

Take blood for example. An important part of blood is common salt. Common salt (NaCl) contains the metal *sodium*.

There is an *iron* compound in red blood cells called *hemoglobin* [HE muh globe in]. Hemoglobin picks up oxygen from the lungs. It then carries the oxygen to every cell of the body.

The metal *calcium* helps build strong bones and teeth. Calcium is also needed for blood clotting.

Cells have trace amounts of other metals like *magnesium*, *copper*, *zinc*, and *cobalt*. These trace elements help the cells carry out the life functions.

Metals come from the soil in the form of *mineral salts*. Plants take in these minerals. We eat the plants—or the animals that have eaten the plants.

Soil can become "tired." That is, its minerals become used up after years of planting. Farmers add fertilizers to soil. Fertilizers put metals and other nutrients back into the soil.

Metals help in everyday health care. Many products you may find in your medicine cabinet contain metals. Some examples are: talcum powder, calamine lotion, milk of magnesia, Mercurochrome, and Epsom salts. Even soap and toothpaste contain metals.

NAME _____

WHY ARE METALS IMPORTANT?

Figure A shows a very important reason.

A STORY OF JUST *ONE* ATOM OF JUST *ONE* METAL.

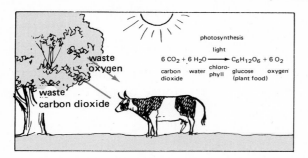

photosynthesis

light

$6\ CO_2 + 6\ H_2O \longrightarrow C_6H_{12}O_6 + 6\ O_2$

carbon   water   chloro-   glucose   oxygen
dioxide   phyll   (plant food)

waste oxygen

waste carbon dioxide

Figure A

Plants make their own food from carbon dioxide and water. Food-making in plants is called *photosynthesis*.

Photosynthesis happens with the aid of sunlight. A green substance called *chlorophyll* must be present in the plant.

The formula for chlorophyll is

$$C_{55}H_{72}O_5N_4Mg$$

1. One molecule of chlorophyll contains 137 atoms. How many of these atoms come from the metal magnesium? _____

2. Can photosynthesis take place without chlorophyll? _____

3. **a)** Why is magnesium important to plants? _____

    _____

    b) Why is magnesium important to people? _____

    _____

A plant takes in magnesium through its roots. It takes in other minerals, too. The minerals include potassium, zinc, iron, copper, and boron.

Figure B

A balanced diet contains all the nutrients a person needs.

Vitamins, minerals, proteins, starches, fats, and oils are nutrients.

Every nutrient contains at least one *metal*.

4. Where do minerals come from? _____

5. Which life form takes in minerals first—plants or animals? _____

6. How do people get their minerals? _____

7. Soil can become "tired." What does tired soil lack? _____

8. What do farmers add to soil to replace minerals? _____

Fertilizers can increase crop size. They can also make poor soil into soil that is good for farming.

9. Why are fertilizers becoming more and more important? _____

_____

Did you ever add "plant food" to the soil of your house plants?

10. Plant "food" isn't really "food." What does it contain? _____

_____

_____

Figure C

COMPLETING SENTENCES

Complete the sentences with the choices below. One of these may be used twice.

sodium	soil	iron
photosynthesis	magnesium	mineral salts
plants	blood	animals
oxygen	calcium	

1. Plants take in metals from the _____ in the form of _____.

2. We get our minerals (metals) by eating _____ or _____ that have eaten plants.

3. The metal in common table salt is _____.

4. Dissolved sodium chloride is an important part of _____.

5. Hemoglobin contains the metal _____.

6. Hemoglobin picks up and delivers _____ to the cells.

7. The metal that helps build strong bones and teeth is _____.

8. Chlorophyll contains the metal _____.

9. Chlorophyll is needed for food-making in plants. This is called _____.

10. Plants give us food and _____.

NAME _____

MATCHING

Match the two lists. Write the correct letter on the line next to each number.

1. _____ photosynthesis

2. _____ calcium

3. _____ roots

4. _____ fertilizers

5. _____ iron

a) part of hemoglobin

b) add minerals to soil

c) helps blood clotting

d) the parts of plants that take in dissolved minerals

e) food-making in plants

NAMING METALS

Four common health aids are shown below. Each one contains at least one metal. Name that metal (or metals). (Do *not* include carbon or hydrogen.)

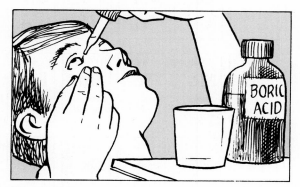

Figure D

1. Boric Acid $(C_2H_5)B(OH)_2$

   Metal _____

Figure E

2. Mercurochrome $C_{20}H_8O_6Na_2Br_2Hg$

   Metals _____

   _____

Figure F

3. Calamine lotion $ZnCO_3$

   Metal _____

Figure G

4. Milk of Magnesia $Mg(OH)_2$

   Metal _____

167

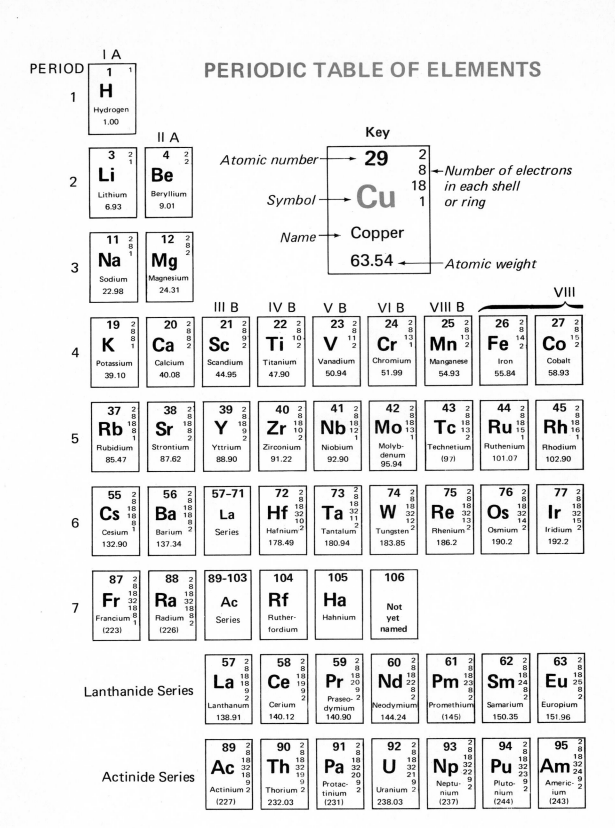

PERIODIC TABLE OF ELEMENTS

PERIOD

I A

1 1
H
Hydrogen
1.00

Key

Atomic number → **29** 2
8
18
Symbol → **Cu** 1 ← *Number of electrons in each shell or ring*

Name → Copper

63.54 ← *Atomic weight*

II A

2
3 2 1
Li
Lithium
6.93

4 2 2
Be
Beryllium
9.01

3
11 2 8 1
Na
Sodium
22.98

12 2 8 2
Mg
Magnesium
24.31

VIII

III B | **IV B** | **V B** | **VI B** | **VIII B** | |

4
19 2 8 8 1
K
Potassium
39.10

20 2 8 8 2
Ca
Calcium
40.08

21 2 8 9 2
Sc
Scandium
44.95

22 2 8 10 2
Ti
Titanium
47.90

23 2 8 11 2
V
Vanadium
50.94

24 2 8 13 1
Cr
Chromium
51.99

25 2 8 13 2
Mn
Manganese
54.93

26 2 8 14 2
Fe
Iron
55.84

27 2 8 15 2
Co
Cobalt
58.93

5
37 2 8 18 8 1
Rb
Rubidium
85.47

38 2 8 18 8 2
Sr
Strontium
87.62

39 2 8 18 9 2
Y
Yttrium
88.90

40 2 8 18 10 2
Zr
Zirconium
91.22

41 2 8 18 12 1
Nb
Niobium
92.90

42 2 8 18 13 1
Mo
Molyb-
denum
95.94

43 2 8 18 13 2
Tc
Technetium
(97)

44 2 8 18 15 1
Ru
Ruthenium
101.07

45 2 8 18 16 1
Rh
Rhodium
102.90

6
55 2 8 18 18 8 1
Cs
Cesium
132.90

56 2 8 18 18 8 2
Ba
Barium
137.34

57-71
La
Series

72 2 8 18 32 10 2
Hf
Hafnium
178.49

73 2 8 18 32 11 2
Ta
Tantalum
180.94

74 2 8 18 32 12 2
W
Tungsten
183.85

75 2 8 18 32 13 2
Re
Rhenium
186.2

76 2 8 18 32 14 2
Os
Osmium
190.2

77 2 8 18 32 15 2
Ir
Iridium
192.2

7
87 2 8 18 32 18 8 1
Fr
Francium
(223)

88 2 8 18 32 18 8 2
Ra
Radium
(226)

89-103
Ac
Series

104
Rf
Ruther-
fordium

105
Ha
Hahnium

106
Not
yet
named

Lanthanide Series

57 2 8 18 18 9 2
La
Lanthanum
138.91

58 2 8 18 19 9 2
Ce
Cerium
140.12

59 2 8 18 20 9 2
Pr
Praseo-
dymium
140.90

60 2 8 18 22 8 2
Nd
Neodymium
144.24

61 2 8 18 23 8 2
Pm
Promethium
(145)

62 2 8 18 24 8 2
Sm
Samarium
150.35

63 2 8 18 25 8 2
Eu
Europium
151.96

Actinide Series

89 2 8 18 32 18 9 2
Ac
Actinium
(227)

90 2 8 18 32 19 9 2
Th
Thorium
232.03

91 2 8 18 32 20 9 2
Pa
Protac-
tinium
(231)

92 2 8 18 32 21 9 2
U
Uranium
238.03

93 2 8 18 32 22 9 2
Np
Neptu-
nium
(237)

94 2 8 18 32 23 9 2
Pu
Pluto-
nium
(244)

95 2 8 18 32 24 9 2
Am
Americ-
ium
(243)

NAME _____

168

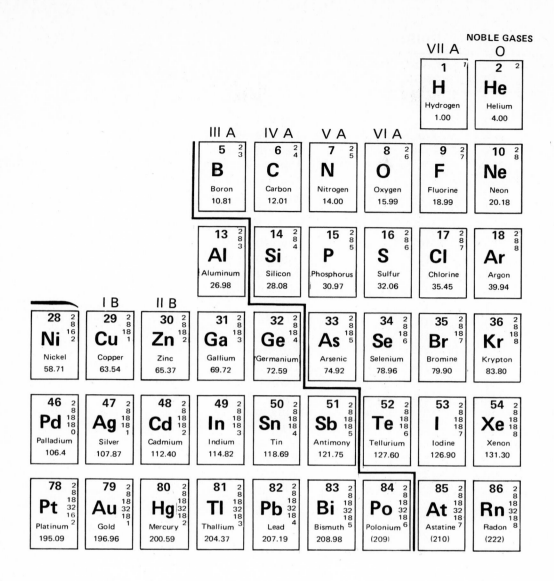

NOBLE GASES

			VII A	O
			1 (2,1) H Hydrogen 1.00	**2** (2) He Helium 4.00

III A	IV A	V A	VI A		
5 (2,3) B Boron 10.81	**6** (2,4) C Carbon 12.01	**7** (2,5) N Nitrogen 14.00	**8** (2,6) O Oxygen 15.99	**9** (2,7) F Fluorine 18.99	**10** (2,8) Ne Neon 20.18
13 (2,8,3) Al Aluminum 26.98	**14** (2,8,4) Si Silicon 28.08	**15** (2,8,5) P Phosphorus 30.97	**16** (2,8,6) S Sulfur 32.06	**17** (2,8,7) Cl Chlorine 35.45	**18** (2,8,8) Ar Argon 39.94

I B	II B						
28 (2,8,16,2) Ni Nickel 58.71	**29** (2,8,18,1) Cu Copper 63.54	**30** (2,8,18,2) Zn Zinc 65.37	**31** (2,8,18,3) Ga Gallium 69.72	**32** (2,8,18,4) Ge Germanium 72.59	**33** (2,8,18,5) As Arsenic 74.92	**34** (2,8,18,6) Se Selenium 78.96	**35** (2,8,18,7) Br Bromine 79.90	**36** (2,8,18,8) Kr Krypton 83.80
46 (2,8,18,0) Pd Palladium 106.4	**47** (2,8,18,1) Ag Silver 107.87	**48** (2,8,18,2) Cd Cadmium 112.40	**49** (2,8,18,3) In Indium 114.82	**50** (2,8,18,4) Sn Tin 118.69	**51** (2,8,18,5) Sb Antimony 121.75	**52** (2,8,18,6) Te Tellurium 127.60	**53** (2,8,18,7) I Iodine 126.90	**54** (2,8,18,8) Xe Xenon 131.30
78 (2,8,18,32,16,2) Pt Platinum 195.09	**79** (2,8,18,32,18,1) Au Gold 196.96	**80** (2,8,18,32,18,2) Hg Mercury 200.59	**81** (2,8,18,32,18,3) Tl Thallium 204.37	**82** (2,8,18,32,18,4) Pb Lead 207.19	**83** (2,8,18,32,18,5) Bi Bismuth 208.98	**84** (2,8,18,32,18,6) Po Polonium (209)	**85** (2,8,18,32,18,7) At Astatine (210)	**86** (2,8,18,32,18,8) Rn Radon (222)

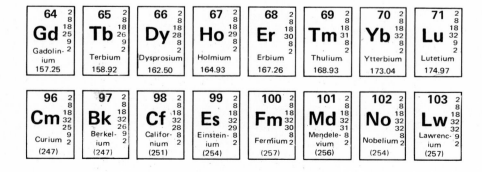

64 (2,8,18,25,9,2) Gd Gadolin- ium 157.25	**65** (2,8,18,26,9,2) Tb Terbium 158.92	**66** (2,8,18,28,2) Dy Dysprosium 162.50	**67** (2,8,18,29,2) Ho Holmium 164.93	**68** (2,8,18,30,8) Er Erbium 167.26	**69** (2,8,18,31,8,2) Tm Thulium 168.93	**70** (2,8,18,32,8,2) Yb Ytterbium 173.04	**71** (2,8,18,32,9,2) Lu Lutetium 174.97
96 (2,8,18,32,25,9,2) Cm Curium (247)	**97** (2,8,18,32,26,9,2) Bk Berkel- ium (247)	**98** (2,8,18,32,28,2) Cf Califor- nium (251)	**99** (2,8,18,32,29,2) Es Einstein- ium (254)	**100** (2,8,18,32,30,8,2) Fm Fermium (257)	**101** (2,8,18,32,31,8,2) Md Mendele- vium (256)	**102** (2,8,18,32,32,2) No Nobelium (254)	**103** (2,8,18,32,32,9,2) Lw Lawrenc- ium (257)

LIST OF ATOMIC WEIGHTS

NAME	SYMBOL	ATOMIC NUMBER	ATOMIC WEIGHT	NAME	SYMBOL	ATOMIC NUMBER	ATOMIC WEIGHT
Hydrogen	H	1	1	Cesium	Cs	55	133
Helium	He	2	4	Barium	Ba	56	137
Lithium	Li	3	7	Lanthanum	La	57	139
Beryllium	Be	4	9	Cerium	Ce	58	140
Boron	B	5	11	Praseodymium	Pr	59	141
Carbon	C	6	12	Neodymium	Nd	60	144
Nitrogen	N	7	14	Promethium	Pm	61	145
Oxygen	O	8	16	Samarium	Sm	62	150
Fluorine	F	9	19	Europium	Eu	63	152
Neon	Ne	10	20	Gadolinium	Gd	64	157
Sodium	Na	11	23	Terbium	Tb	65	159
Magnesium	Mg	12	24	Dysprosium	Dy	66	163
Aluminum	Al	13	27	Holmium	Ho	67	165
Silicon	Si	14	28	Erbium	Er	68	167
Phosphorus	P	15	31	Thullium	Tm	69	169
Sulfur	S	16	32	Ytterbium	Yb	70	173
Chlorine	Cl	17	35	Lutetium	Lu	71	175
Argon	Ar	18	40	Hafnium	Hf	72	178
Potassium	K	19	39	Tantalum	Ta	73	181
Calcium	Ca	20	40	Tungsten	W	74	184
Scandium	Sc	21	45	Rhenium	Re	75	186
Titanium	Ti	22	48	Osmium	Os	76	190
Vanadium	V	23	51	Iridium	Ir	77	192
Chromium	Cr	24	52	Platinum	Pt	78	195
Manganese	Mn	25	55	Gold	Au	79	197
Iron	Fe	26	56	Mercury	Hg	80	201
Cobalt	Co	27	59	Thallium	Tl	81	204
Nickel	Ni	28	59	Lead	Pb	82	207
Copper	Cu	29	64	Bismuth	Bi	83	209
Zinc	Zn	30	65	Polonium	Po	84	209
Gallium	Ga	31	70	Astatine	At	85	210
Germanium	Ge	32	73	Radon	Rn	86	222
Arsenic	As	33	75	Francium	Fr	87	223
Selenium	Se	34	79	Radium	Ra	88	226
Bromine	Br	35	80	Actinium	Ac	89	227
Krypton	Kr	36	84	Thorium	Th	90	232
Rubidium	Rb	37	85	Protactinium	Pa	91	231
Strontium	Sr	38	88	Uranium	U	92	238
Yttrium	Y	39	89	Neptunium	Np	93	237
Zirconium	Zr	40	91	Plutonium	Pu	94	244
Niobium	Nb	41	93	Americium	Am	95	243
Molybdenum	Mo	42	96	Curium	Cm	96	247
Technetium	Te	43	97	Berkelium	Bk	97	247
Ruthenium	Ru	44	101	Californium	Cf	98	251
Rhodium	Rh	45	103	Einsteinium	Es	99	254
Palladium	Pd	46	106	Fermium	Fm	100	257
Silver	Ag	47	108	Mendeluvium	Md	101	256
Cadmium	Cd	48	112	Nobelium	No	102	254
Indium	In	49	115	Lawrencium	Lw	103	257
Tin	Sn	50	119	Rutherfordium	Rf	104	*
Antimony	Sb	51	122	Hahnium	Ha	105	*
Tellurium	Te	52	128	* *	* *	106	*
Iodine	I	53	127				
Xenon	Xe	54	131				

*Information not yet available

* * Not yet named